SMELLY HEARING AIDS

AND

FISHY LIPS

SMELLY HEARING AIDS

AND

FISHY LIPS

A Deaf Teenager's Journal

Marc Heyez

ISBN-13: 978-0-9951532-0-2
Legal deposit 2016
Library and Archives Canada, Ottawa

Gervais, Marc 1968-, author
    Smelly Hearing Aids and Fishy Lips: A deaf teenager's journal/Marc Heyez.

ISBN-13: 978-0-9951532-0-2 (paperback)

Cover and back cover created by Marc Gervais through CreateSpace

BISAC: Humor/general

This book is dedicated to my brother, Matt, who provided insightful comments and wise advice on improving this book and to my wife, Nathalie, who tirelessly reminded, pushed and threatened me with small furry animals to get this manuscript finally published.

January 1983

Saturday, January 1st: New Year's Day. Last night was a story of lust, deception, panic and one unused condom in my pocket. It began yesterday afternoon when a gorgeous dark-haired girl invited me to a private New Year's Eve party at Queen's restaurant bar. Since I didn't want to be a dork and in a molecule-small remote chance I would be driving her to the nearest hotel afterwards, I "borrowed" my sister's car while she was out with a college turd. I didn't have a driver's licence and my parents were away at another party.

I managed to remember and use the 2.5 hours of driving instructions from my traumatized father to drive myself downtown Montreal at speeds rivalling an ice cream truck. I parked my sister's car in a way a car should never be parked and waited for the girl inside the smoke-filled restaurant-bar. Three hours, nine glasses of Coke and two blackened lungs later, it dawns on me—the girl was never going to show up. I left with a heavy heart. Walking across the parking lot, I saw a big empty space where the car had been parked haphazardly. Stolen! I staggered to a corner and several cups of the aforementioned Coke were ejected onto the snow bank. It was 2:30 a.m. and I went home on a special late-night bus occupied by one other passenger, a drunkenly happy dishevelled longhaired man wearing a bright green parka.

A fierce shaking woke me up this morning and being half-asleep, I turned over but the shaking continued. The blanket was ripped away and a beating of fists rained upon my skinny chest. Giving in, I peeped out of my groggy eyes and they snapped open like broken roller blinds: It was the ugly dishevelled long-haired man with a bright green parka! No—it was my sister. Close enough. Ilisha was silently screaming at me, mouthing her words in fury. I plugged in my hearing aids and the peaceful silence was stabbed by her shrill voice.

1

"—My car? What did you do to my car? Where is it?"

Car? The morning light was bright and my mind was dim. As I squinted at my pissed off sibling, the blurry reality of last night came into clear focus and I scrambled for an explanation. I had to be honest. "It was stolen last night."

"Stolen? My Honda? What? What happened?" Her grip on my sailboat pyjamas tightened.

"Uh, I was home all night and right before I went up to bed, I saw a strange man tip toeing through the living room and once he saw me, he bolted out the front door and sped off with your car."

My parents, to my alarm, took my story with dead seriousness and drove me to the police station to file a report. A skinny cop escorted me to a small room in the back of the station, the kind they use to interrogate hardened suspects. I sat on a cold chair bolted to the floor and repeated the story I had told Ilisha and my parents, making sure I kept all details consistent. Inconsistent storytelling will invite suspicion. After my story, he began to shoot me with questions. I couldn't lip-read him through his standard cop mustache partially hiding his lips. He became frustrated with repeating his questions so many times that Mum had to be brought in to translate. I had to be creative in answering one question: "What is the description of the intruder?" The chances of him asking this question was the same as finding a broken potato chip in a party bowl.

"Uh, he was an ugly dishevelled long-haired man wearing a bright green parka." Better him than me. He made me look through a thick mug shot book but I couldn't "find" his picture. Lots of scary fellows in there, their looks alone would be enough for me to fork over my cash in absence of any weapons.

Back home, we looked for other stolen items, but found nothing missing.

"Thank gawd, nothing else was taken," Mum said in her American twang.

"Brilliant! And, my rare book collection is untouched," Father noted in his stuffy British accent.

"They didn't touch my money on the dresser," Ilisha mentioned.

After we all settled down, Ilisha was on her way out on a date with the same geek as the night before. As she was putting on her coat, she frowned at my snow boots, her eyes narrowing. "Egg, if you didn't go out last night, why were your boots wet?"

My neck felt hot and I stammered, "I, I, I tried to chase your car after the bad guy drove off."

"Strange—you didn't mention that before," she said before shutting the door. The noose of guilt tightened.

I went into my room, sat at my desk and I made six New Year's resolutions:

1. I shall not procrastinate. Writing this resolution list today and not halfway through the year is a start.

2. Since this is my last year of high school, I'll go to Aviation College this fall and work hard to achieve my life-long dream of becoming a pilot.

3. I shall find myself a girlfriend before I turn 18. If I don't achieve this goal, I'll become sexually enamored with inanimate objects such as telephone poles, if what my friend Luderick says is true.

4. I shall start bodybuilding for real—no more wimpy push-ups. My body resembles a poorly drawn stick-man figure and I must uphold the Canadian image of the burly bearded lumberjack for the world. Pet moose and beer would be optional.

5. I shall write a daily journal of my life and thoughts as a hearing impaired teen.

6. I shall stick to this New Year's resolution list like a bug on flypaper in an obscure middle-of-the-road greasy spoon.

This is pretty much the same list of resolutions as it has been for the past three years. This is a do-or-die year, especially the girlfriend part. Turning 18 is a rite of passage into manhood and I want all the ingredients of a real man—a girl on my arm, wide shoulders and a Beaver bush plane in the driveway to boot. Sexual experience would be a bonus.

Why did the gorgeous dark-haired girl invite me and not show up at the restaurant-bar? Was she serious or was she playing a joke on a hearing aid wearing skinny guy? I must be a damn fool.

Sunday, January 2: After dinner, I walked to Luderick's house with my hockey stick and orange ball. Before I rang the doorbell, my friend opened the timeworn door with utmost quietness. "Hey Egg, what's up?" he whispered.

"Hey Luderick, let's play hockey, eh?" I rasped.

"Cool man, let me put on my goalie stuff," he said. "Don't make any noise—my ma is praying again." He quietly led me through his dark and gloomy home. The heavy shades were drawn, lights were off and spooky candles flickered upon the holy paintings on the dirty white walls. We crept down the creaky stairs to the damp and musty basement. While Luderick strapped on his goalie equipment among the 1970s decor, I gazed at the religious paintings depicting Jesus, Mary, assorted saints and momentous awe-inspiring scenes hung everywhere along with dozens of rosaries. I've once counted 13 different art works of The Last Supper including one made out of macaroni glued on cardboard paper made by Luderick when he was eight. A large collection of dusty vintage Bibles lined along the back cement wall, its titles faded and bindings so weak that a good sneeze would blow them apart.

"Good insulation," Luderick mumbled. "Ok, I'm ready, let's go."

Shuffling through the house, scraping and bumping the walls as if he was a suited-up deep sea diver going to the ship's head, Luderick's gangly goalie stick swung here and there and knocked over a Mary figurine, one of hundreds of religious figurines carefully placed on the many shelves, steps and counter tops. Luderick's mother burst out of her special prayer room with much fury and gave him an earful.

"How many times do I've to tell you not to knock over my precious statues? Why do you have to play that violent game? What are you doing with the stick I threw out?" She shrilled on and on, much of which was garbled to my innocent ears. While she was harping on, I peeked into her prayer room and saw a shrine where the density and number of candles was enough to give the Dionne quintuplets a 50th birthday party.

"You gotta forgive my mom," Luderick said as we shuffled through the snow outside. "She's getting way too hung up on the Jesus stuff. Christ, I'm her only social life. She spends huge chunks of her time doing religious things. Every day, I mean every day, man, she prays in that room for two solid hours after dinner and cannot be disturbed."

Mental note: never visit him again after dinner. Luderick is not so religious. He once quipped, "I never follow the stuff, I'm an agnostic insomniac with dyslexia: I lie awake nights wondering if there is a dog."

However, his mom still drags him to Church every Sunday morning. He often complains, "At eight in the damn morning! On a weekend no less! Hell, what normal teenager goes to mass so early?"

We played one–on–one street hockey with Luderick in net pretending to be famed Montreal Canadiens goalie Jacques Plante and I took slap shots on him as Bernie "Boom Boom" Geoffrion. "Boom Boom" was the sound made when I missed the net and the frozen ball ricocheted off cars, living-room windows and the garage door. "*Câlisse, tabernac! Pas encore!*" Jacques Plante cursed each time he had to fetch the ball. We played for an hour and shuffled inside after the ball was shot high on his roof and it rolled into the eaves trough.

Over a cup of hot chocolate, Luderick talked about a conspiracy he'd heard about. He does this every time we meet. This time, he explained the many possible conspiracies behind John F. Kennedy's assassination on November 22, 1963. It was fascinating but I found it frustrating the truth would never be known given the many suspicious details swirling about this case. Luderick, using his sharp deductive mind, offered a unique theory: Kennedy's fatal wound was caused by an imploded sneeze. "You can see in the Zapruder film that JFK had his hands in front of his mouth as if he was stifling a sneeze." I told him Lee Harvey Oswald was guilty because he had three names as other infamous killers in history such as John Wilkes Booth, Mark David Chapman and John Wayne Gacy.

Luderick is the only real friend I have. He's doesn't mind my hearing impairment and genuinely thinks it's cool.

His first words when we met were, "Hey neat-o, those hearing aids make you look like a secret service man for the president." I think I'm his only friend. Luderick was in my geometry class at Canterbury two years ago and was expelled for refusing to abide the school's suit-and-tie dress code. Canterbury is a private all-boys high school run by dictators and has a policy book several volumes wide. To make a political statement, Luderick would arrive to class in Smurf pyjamas. He claims that, "Ties are useless strips of fabric that do nothing but finance the fashion industry and choke you when you stand too close to a paper shredder."

We tend to meet on Sunday afternoons, usually to play street hockey and shoot the breeze. His father ran off with the milkman when he was five and Luderick, an only child, has lived with his mother ever since. He's paranoid about the government, the capitalist system and the military; a large base of his knowledge is taken up by assorted conspiracies that may or may not be true. He's a prophet who rants and raves that the world will end on Tuesday but makes an appointment with a doctor on Thursday.

I came home at 10:30 pm, munched on a peanut butter and banana sandwich and prepared to go to bed. While I was brushing my teeth, Ilisha cornered me in the bathroom, "You know, Egg, I've been thinking," her eyes laser-beamed me, "How come you smelled of cigarette smoke yesterday morning when I woke you up? Are you sure you didn't go out at all on New Year's Eve?"

"Uh, no," I took a deep breath. "Luderick came over and smoked a whole pack of cigarettes to celebrate New Year's."

"Hmmm, I don't remember the house smelling of smoke."

I said nothing and continued to brush. She squinted at me and left. Damn! She's on to me! The noose tightens more.

Once I finished brushing, I checked my face for any signs of manly facial hair. Nothing. It's disheartening to know that my grandmother has more facial hair than I do.

Monday, January 3: During supper, Dad, a psychiatrist at the Huchen Mental Institute, told me about an interesting case of a female patient with hyperacusis.

Hyperacusis, he explained, is a rare disorder that causes people to have the most acute sense of hearing. "D.B." was a woman who was able to hear the softest of sounds. Ordinary noises sounded as loud as a cannon-shot and she could hear the ticking of a watch up to nine metres away. My Dad and D.B. would meet in a soundproof room and communicate by writing. Her problem wasn't related to being sensitive to sound but dealing with the attitudes of ignorant people around her. Most people don't know what "hyperacusis" means and were not empathetic nor accommodating. They would shout, "What do you mean? I'm talking too low?" My dad successfully treated her by using a personal relations technique and treatment terminated once she became more confident in dealing with the loud idiots in her life.

I find it unfair that, similar to wealth, some people have too much of something and some have too little. I wish D.B. could give me a part of her hearing because I'm sorely lacking in this department. We would be an interesting couple, though. Our differences in hearing would complement each other. I would go around saying, "What? I can't hear." And she would say, "Shhhhh. Not so loud."

After Dad's story, he retired in the cherrywood-panelled den to sit in his favourite leather chair to read, "*Phonetic Feature Definitions and Their Integration into Phonology and*

Their Relation to Speech: A case study of a buck-toothed Latvian farmer with sinus congestion." I put on my faux R.C.A.F. bomber jacket and cleared the snow off our driveway by myself. I don't mind shovelling, as it gives me time to peacefully mull over thought-provoking questions under the clear starry sky, such as wondering why biblical Adam was depicted in paintings as having a belly button?

Once I cleared the driveway, I worked on the De Havilland Mosquito WWII plane model I received for Christmas. So far, I've glued together six propeller blades and a few other smaller pieces.

Wednesday, January 5: True to my New Year's resolution to resemble a burly Canadian lumberjack (also, you never see a skinny R.C.A.F. pilot), I joined the bodybuilding club at the community centre. A muscle-bound ape of a man gave me a quick tour of the facilities which looked more of a 17th century torture dungeon than a so-called fitness room it calls itself. A scary place to be. It's filled with straining, bulky, masochistic men in stained T-shirts inflicting pain on themselves with assorted clanking contraptions complete with moving chains and levers.

I gulped hard, breathed in deeply and did my first difficult repetition—I lifted my wallet and paid the club fee. I'll start tomorrow. I hope it's not a problem if I signed the bodily damage and injury waiver form using my cat's name.

The gym also had free weights, so I took some home.

When I told Mum about the bodybuilding club, she waved me off and said, "Egg, don't bother me now, I need to prepare fer an important job interview tomorra." She was watering her plants at the time and I'm not sure if this was considered as "preparing for a job interview." She's a career job hunter; it has been two years since she lost her job as a hair dresser and has been going to the employment bureau often enough to trade birthday cards with the employment counselors. The many job application forms she has filled out are enough to clear all the trees on a small B.C. island. She has suffered through so many job interviews that she can tell from the arrangement of pencils on an employer's desk if they clean behind their refrigerator every three months.

School starts in five days. Yuck. I have a vague recollection I'm required to give an oral presentation for class on the first day. Too much eggnog, the intoxicating smell of the dead pine tree in our living room and excess Bing Crosby Christmas music have muddied my mind.

Out of guilt and to get my sister off my back, I told her I've decided to check with the police station every few days or so to see if they've found her car "as a favour."

"You better get my car back, " she threatened.

"I had nothing to do with it!" I protested.

I'll start tomorrow.

Thursday, January 6: I can barely lift my pen to write today's journal entry. I worked out today at the dungeon for the first time and the no-neck ape-man forced me do a weight lifting routine for two solid hours. All my muscles are sore, even the ones I didn't know I had. Worst of all, I have to do this three times a week. I may be sore today, "but just you wait 'til tomorrow mornin'," the ape-man grinned.

After the workout, I dragged myself to the police station to ask the skinny cop about Ilisha's car. After glancing through a long list in his binder, he said, "Nope, not in."

Mum's interview didn't go well this morning. When she trudged home, she plopped herself in front of the TV and wasted the rest of the afternoon watching a Tibetan musical about dancing yaks.

Since Mum wasn't in the mood to cook supper, Dad ordered two pizzas and we ate with Ilisha's new boyfriend, a graduate student in electrical engineering with graceful, well-heeled social skills of a keyboard. She's only dating him because he's "filthy rich." Money has a way of covering up a face full of zits. Since I never caught his name, I shall refer him as "Dweeby." Playing her motherly role to the hilt, Mum joined us and drilled him with questions. He never looked up from his plate and spent the entire evening directing his answers to his slice of pizza. From Dweeby's incoherent mumbles, I could tell they were one-word answers. Ilisha would elaborate his responses with details of his previous work (Hydro-Electric intern at James Bay), future aspirations (creating software for power grids) and hobbies (collecting old power breakers). I don't see how Ilisha was able to pump this much information from him in the past two weeks they've been dating. After dessert, they quietly sat together and listened to Ilisha's favourite country and western music album, "I sat down on a bear trap (just this morning)." I kept my body and fragile mind in another part of the house.

Friday, January 7: I now know the meaning of "pain." What it has to do with "gain" is beyond me. My muscles, or what's left of them, are sore and numb beyond description. I couldn't even get out of my bed this morning! Mum told me to rest in bed and let my muscles recuperate. She had to hand-feed me Galaga pop cereal because I couldn't lift my arms. You know how astronomers say that a neutron star has matter so dense and heavy that a spoonful of it weighs several thousand tons? Well, this was the spoon I tried using this morning.

Before Mum left for the employment office, she brought in the old 12-inch black and white TV and put it on my dresser so I could watch it from my bed. Normally, I don't watch much TV because I have little clue as to what they're saying. I tend to stick to visual shows such as hockey games and Roadrunner cartoons. Since I was too sore to get up to change the channel, I was stuck with "*The Hippy Happy Times of Hoppy the Hamster*" cartoon festival. It's virtually impossible to lip-read cartoon characters. Their so-called lips, if they have any, hardly match what they say.

Saturday, January 8: I'm sick today. Mum pronounced me sick when she caught me "driving the porcelain bus" at 4:30 a.m. I was wobbly as a drunk, weak as a kitten and pale as Keith Richards.

Despite my deathly pallor, Mrs. Tautog from the Montreal Oral School for the Deaf still came over to do her speech therapy lessons. Ugh. I've been spending one hour every week for the past six years with this speech therapist, trying to clearly and accurately repeat words coming out of the wobbly, wrinkly, wide mouth of an old fish. Not only that, this old fish always comes in the middle of a Saturday afternoon when I should be living out the average teenager's life which consists of sleeping until 1:00 in the afternoon and doing nothing for the rest of the day. Today, I sat on my aching butt at the kitchen table in my bathrobe and, with a big box of tissues beside me, I sniffled and groaned throughout the lesson, trying to look pathetic enough to make her shorten it. Today was no different; she resolutely stuck to her 60-minute schedule. I could be on my deathbed, my life slipping away and she would be sitting by my side, as rigid as a Popsicle stick, saying, "Now, repeat after me, 'Isp isp isp'."

On the other hand, she's an okay woman and I do try to improve my voice so I can ask girls for dates without sounding like a snooty Frenchman with a cold.

When Mrs. Tautog finally waddled off, I crawled up the stairs to go back to bed. Mum and Dad had to drive Ilisha to her volleyball practice and I was left alone. This was when I experienced one of those annoying moments as a hearing impaired person—the phone right next to my bedroom door rang many times. Why does Mum put the ring volume so damn loud? She knows I never answer it when no one is home since the phone is as useful to me as a sandbox to a desert dweller. With no lips to read, all I hear are garbles, burbles and murmurs interspersed with vague-sounding words. Besides, no one ever calls me and sometimes it's one of Dad's patients calling. I don't want to be on the phone alone with a lunatic threatening to suffocate himself with Q-tips while stapling himself to the bathroom wall. But, whenever the phone rings, doubts always nag me. What if it's a serious emergency? What if the sweepstakes are calling?

School starts on the day after tomorrow. Oh, joy!

Sunday, January 9: Was sick all day again. I watched more TV but no cartoons. Understanding real actors are just as bad. Their lips don't stay in one place long enough for me to lip-read; they yell off-screen, turn their heads away and cry too much. This is the last time I watch soap operas.

When no one was home, I dragged myself out of the house, took the bus to the police station in throes of death and asked the skinny cop about Ilisha's car. He had the same response—"Nope, not in."

Mum caught me walking in the front door and pronounced me recovered and well enough to go to school tomorrow. Damn! I gave a coughing fit worthy of an Academy Award but she didn't back down. Furthermore, she cut my hair in preparation for school because regulations state that hair cannot be lower than the student's earlobes.

I did feel better. I worked on the De Havilland Mosquito model but had to stop when the glue began to make me feel dizzy.

Monday, January 10: School started today. Since I take my hearing aids off when I go to bed and don't hear a sound unless someone says I've won a million dollars, Mum wakes me up every damn morning. She gives me one chance, so if I go back to sleep after she has poked me, I've to "live with th' consequences" which is getting detention for every class I miss.

This morning I checked my body for any symptoms of a slightly fatal contagious diseases and, much to my disappointment, found none.

Once again this term, I used the FM system for class. My teachers clip a small microphone to their jacket lapels and I attach the receiver boot to my hearing aid with the wire snaking under my cardigan to the processor box on my belt. This way, their voices are transmitted directly into my hearing aid via radio waves and I lose no clarity when the teacher moves about the classroom, even when old Mr. Acipenser goes to the bathroom. In a class of normal-hearing students, it advertises my deafness similar to an ugly blinking strip-bar neon sign on wet night. I can tolerate it as long as the wire doesn't catch on something and strangle me if I jump out the window after someone talks too much about Third World poverty.

Remember I had a vague memory of an assignment to do? Well, I learned I was supposed to prepare for a five-minute oral presentation for public speaking class today. I was listed as the fourth person to give a speech. Akin to those with last names that start with a "Z" in a roll call, I suffered through the agony of waiting. I was hoping each of the three speakers before me would give long and slow speeches so there would be no time left for me. No such luck. My anxiety and sweat mounted as each speaker zipped through their presentations. When Todd finished his talk about stimulus-response eye reaction time in South African armadillos, Mr. Bonito yelled out my name, his huge walrus mustache puffing out. I cringed and stumbled up in front of 30 pairs of staring eyes. Totally unprepared, I took a wise course of action—I winged it. I ad-libbed a philosophic piece on how the smallest element cannot exist because of the mathematical ability of dividing something in half forever. If you found the smallest electron on an atom, I can find an even smaller element by chopping it in half, chopping the half into a half and so on infinitely. To give it more credence, I spoke in my best authoritative hearing impaired voice, if a squeaky rusted bike voice could be authoritative.

After my speech, it was Alfonsino's turn. Let me tell you about him: put all the outmoded porno back-page "How to pick up women" attitudes in a small five-foot-two Lebanese with a cheesy see-through first-timer moustache and you will have Alfonsino.

He swaggered up in front of class in his usual threads: paisley purple tie, pastel blue shirt with jumbo airplane collars, a black jacket with wings of equal flying ability and tight Notre-Dame cathedral bell-bottom pants over a pair of blocky platform shoes. Even if he appears to be a disoriented leftover extra from the filming of "Saturday Night Fever," the school board cannot discipline him for bad taste as long as he follows the dress code.

Our fashion nightmare put aside three rolled-up posters and announced, "Today, my presentation is called 'The female human species.' First, I'll tell you guys about the female body..." Mr. Bonito stopped him a mere second before he went into graphic detail about differently shaped breasts.

15

"Hey, teach, this is valuable information," he protested and earned himself two detentions and a zilch on his assignment. We never saw his presentation posters.

As I write this, I'm pissed off at Ilisha. She used up all my shampoo and I had to wash my hair with hand soap before bed. Thankfully, Canterbury is an all-boys' school because my hair resembles a mortarboard tassel. I found Ilisha's special hair conditioner under the sink and poured in clear liquid glue and placed the bottle back exactly where I found it.

Tuesday, January 11: It was the second day of school and I already dread waking up in the morning. Waking up early is the one activity you can have a lot of practise doing and never become good at it.

At lunchtime, Jake, being in his usual bad mood, slammed his elbow into a baseball cap. It was Alfonsino's misfortune that he was wearing it at the time. Jake Hammerhead, being seven feet and two inches tall and 429 pounds, is our designated class bully. He can crush a beer can between his pinky and thumb and has fists the size of small bowling balls. He visits headmaster Mr. Sculpin's office so often the goldfish leap out of the bowl every time he enters.

On the way home, I stopped by the police station for a quick visit. Still no car.

When I arrived home, Dad's hands were bandaged and his hair cut short, right to the scalp. Out of his earshot, Mum explained he had an "embarrassin' accident washin' his hair dis mornin'" and she had to drive him to the hospital. They sat in the waiting room for three hours, him looking irate and his hands stuck to his head. "Bloody hell, that's the last time I use hair conditioner," Dad grumbled.

Ilisha's boyfriend Dweeby ate supper with us again. Mum, being a quick learner, refrained from drilling him with questions. He was quiet and only two mumbled words spontaneously emanated from his pimply face. Seeing Dad handing him the salt shaker immediately after, the two sole words must've been "Salt please." Strangely, Dweeby glanced in my direction a few times as if he was about to ask me something but continued to shovel mashed potatoes in his mouth.

After dinner, everyone left to attend Ilisha's volleyball game and I stayed home to assemble the De Havilland Mosquito model. While I was gluing on the wings, the phone rang. I ignored it but it kept on ringing and ringing. After five minutes of inane ringing, I turned my hearing aids off but when I switched them back on half an hour later, it was still ringing!

When the incessant phone continued to ring for another five minutes, I switched my hearing aids to telephone mode and bravely answered it, a move that could only be explained by excessive exposure to airplane glue. It was a man asking for my Dad. When I told him he was out, he said he wanted me to give him a massage.

"I'm hearing impaired and I don't massage my Dad's feet because he has athletes' foot," I said.

"No—garble garble a message! I garble garble your father garble..." and the rest was as clear as an Estonian auctioneer talking underwater. I tried to tell him I didn't understand him but he was persistent, kept repeating his message over and over but all I could decipher was, "Peas, high pigpen dromedary aft go sailing." The more he talked, the more uncomfortable I became. Boy, did I ever want to lose this guy! Out of frustration, I yelled, "I'm deaf!" for the final time and hung up on him. The phone rang again but I dared not answer it. I put on my Bomber jacket while it continued to ring and walked to the community centre to work out.

I forgot tell Dad about the call. It's 11:35 p.m. and he's already asleep. If it was so important, the man will call again.

Wednesday, January 12: Again, I woke up this morning with a half dead body. My muscles didn't protest as much as they did last time because I didn't have the sadistic ape-man torturing me.

I read an interesting story on the front page of today's paper. It says that a mental hospital patient escaped yesterday and sat in the frozen food section of Steinberg's grocery store ranting that separatists are lobbying to separate his nose from his face. The article explains that the patient's doctor, Dr. Rounder, was out of town and couldn't be informed of his escape and his need for medication. Dr. Rounder's colleague, Dr. Snook, attempted to contact the doctor at home but could only reach his son, who was "extremely uncooperative." He was quoted, "I heard him tell me, 'I'm death' and he hung up on me!"

After school, as I stood alone in the bus shelter waiting for my dark ride home, I contemplated about how I'll soon be 18 and that I never had a girlfriend. I know there is one girl among thousands whom I'll fall in love with, marry and have 2.5 children and a house in the suburbs. Is there a girl out there meant for me? Where is she? What is she doing? I wonder what she will look like? How long will I have to wait?

Thursday, January 13: On the crowded bus ride after school, I noticed a sexy dark-haired girl standing near the back glancing at me. I did a double take—she was the girl who stood me up on New Year's Eve! She wore an unidentifiable maroon school uniform underneath a fur coat, was about my age, had long wavy black hair and soft brown eyes. Her blouse was unbuttoned halfway. When the sidelong glances persisted, I quickly checked that my zipper was up and rubbed my face to make sure my chin had no chip crumbs. I squirmed in my warm seat and tried looking away but from the corner of my eyes I kept glimpsing her coy face among the crowd.

At one point I glanced at her, she smiled and sensually mouthed, "Hi." A tingly sensation rushed up my spine. My face hot and flushed, I stared at my feet and felt my temples throbbing. My mind raced with questions. Why is she doing this to me? What do I say? What do I do next? I know—I'll say "Hi" back. I looked up and she disappeared; she had already gotten off the bus! My face dropped. I searched outside for her but only saw Jake breaking into an old American car. Damn! Thinking fast, I studied my watch. Let's see: it was 18 minutes from where I embarked so therefore, I took the 2:55 bus. I shall take the same bus from now on.

While I worked out at the dungeon, I thought about the girl. Why did she invite me to that bar on New Year's and not show up? Did she mean it when she said "Hi"? Was she talking to the guy next to me? The idea of a girl, especially the beautiful kind, showing a modicum of interest in me is incomprehensible. Hearing impaired in a hearing world, I've always felt different. No one would be interested in a defective boy such as me. When the doctor first told my parents about my handicap, he said, "I'm sorry, something is seriously wrong with your boy. He's hearing impaired." My father, for some strange reason, objected to his choice of words and replied, "There is nothing wrong with him—he just can't hear, that's all."

Friday, January 14: I woke up sore from last night's workout, but the dull ache in my muscles is starting to feel good. Mum complained, "Egg, you're becomin' a masochist, you're gonna soon enjoy leather whips, torture racks and fillin' out provincial tax forms."

I had trouble concentrating in class today. All day I daydreamed about the sexy dark-haired girl. As I munched on my sandwich in the cafeteria, I stared in space with a dreamy look on my face and Jake thought I was gazing at him. The big bully slowly turned his head, his beady eyes lowering.

"Egg, you fruit!" he bellowed from the next table. "What the hell you're staring at? I'm gonna punch your nose so far down you will hafta go up yer ass to pick it!" He paused for effect. "And when I'm done, I'm gonna bury you alive."

The cafeteria became uncomfortably quiet. Some put down their Rubik's cubes.

My sandwich froze in the mid-air before my gaping mouth.

I swallowed hard.

My eyes never blinked.

"I'm watching you Jake," Mr. Sculpin said as he passed by.

Jake waited until the headmaster was out of earshot before he scowled at me, "Don't do that again, you poof." When he resumed eating his deer hindquarters, I exhaled for the next two minutes. Thank you Headmaster, for preventing my certain internment.

You know, a hearing aid has a microphone that amplifies sounds to be sent into my ear. A loose-fitting hearing aid will make a squealing feedback in the same manner as a singer's microphone poised near an amplifier. If I was trapped somewhere or buried underground by Jake, I would use my hearing aids to whistle S.O.S. in Morse code. I would either get rescued and be hailed for using hearing aids in an innovative way or have many dogs come running.

Today is Friday and I hate Fridays. It's supposed to be a good day and all, is the last day of the week, starts with "F," and is one of the few words not cursed by sailors. I hate Fridays because it's gym day. As long as our gym teacher, if you can call him that, is around, I'll have nightmares about Fridays until I'm 70 and find myself downtown in my underwear. Mr. Barracuda teaches the most violent and injury-prone sports and would consider it a "bad day" if no one spilled blood or pieces of his brain on the floor. It's a fact hospital admissions tend to be highest on Fridays, a mystery to researchers. Evidently, they didn't consider our gym class. Mr. Barracuda is a miserable man who watches bad American infomercials in his dreary apartment while scraping pitiable remnants of a cold pizza off the bottom of the box on a Saturday night. Bill Bream told me a few years ago that he grew up in a military family and his father was a senior drill sergeant with the Russian army during WWII. He was trained to be tough, to never show weakness and to never, ever wear pink nail polish. Thus, he became someone who sucks happy-go-lucky students into his personal black hole and spits out pathetic, shrivelled up little boys whose penises have retracted into their bodies.

Jake, on the other hand, loves gym because it's the only time he can freely maim someone without getting detention.

The gym is in a separate building from the school and we have to walk outside to get there, even in the winter. To make best of things, I often imagine myself undergoing rigourous training for the R.C.A.F. but it doesn't work for long because the scenery is too bereft of planes and landing strips to keep it realistic-looking. The only decoration in the cavernous gym is the faded 1955–56 basketball championship banner hanging high in the rafters, something we won by default when the opposing team's bus swerved into a ditch during the blizzard of '56. Not too inspiring.

Today we played lacrosse indoors under the aegis of Mr. Barracuda's miserliness. Without any benefit of padded equipment, we did hockey-style crosschecking, hooking and tripping. Jake, much to our goalie's psychological trauma, scored most of the goals for the opposing team. Alfonsino will have nightmares and wet his bed for the next few days.

"Come on, men," Mr. Barracuda boomed after four of us scooted away when Jake charged through. "Play hard, this will put hair on your balls." Playing this sport did the exact opposite, scaring my hair follicles so deep, they won't peep out until I'm 45 and balding.

When the last class bell rang, I ran to the bus stop to take the 2:55 bus home with high hopes of seeing the dark-haired girl again. No luck.

Mum wasn't happy today. "I applied to five different places today an' none of 'em were even remotely interested," she complained. I find it difficult to understand why no one would hire such a nice person as my Mum. If I were the boss of a giant company, I'd hire her to be my personal secretary in a heartbeat.

Tabernac! I keep forgetting to stop by the police station. I'll try to go on Monday.

Saturday, January 15: I had a strange dream last night. I was hired by the R.C.M.P. to sit in an unmarked car to lip-read a mobster giving information on the next drug shipment over a public phone. To my luck, the mobster's face was turned away and I couldn't read his lips but I observed he was gesturing frantically. After watching him whipping his arms around, the detective asked me, "Well? What did he say?"

I said, "I'm not sure, he's either trying to dry out his armpits or he's practicing his airplane signals."

I thought of something interesting about dreams. You know how we sometimes dream in black and white and sometimes in colour? Since the concept of black and white came from the invention of photography, did people before this time presumably always dreamt in colour?

Mrs. Tautog didn't answer my question, she pursed her wrinkled lips and said, "We will work on our 'B' and 'P' sounds today." Even with my hearing aids cranked up high, I could barely hear the difference between these letters and words such as "Ben" and "Pen" look the damn same on the lips. I'm unsure as to which word I heard unless I have a context—a sentence to go with it. For example, "I stabbed Ben with a pen." I had the urge to do this after 60 minutes of this inane exercise.

Sunday, January 16: Luderick came over to my place after church and the first thing he did was to look around as if he misplaced his hat.

"You can stop looking for her. My sister is not here."

"Oh," he sighed. "Is she dating anyone now?"

"She's going out with some pizza-faced college guy with articulation skills of a constipated elephant."

He sighed mournfully. We went out and played street hockey despite the blustery -22 °C temperature because toughing out the cold will transform us spindly little boys into big, burly Canadian men. After ten minutes, we went back inside after Luderick's asthma began to act up. In my room, Luderick told me in his usual animated manner about a possible conspiracy, this time involving breakfast cereals.

"Okay, you know how most cereals float, eh? Did you ever notice when we eat it, we tend to spoon it off the top and what happens? Bam! Before you know it, you're left with no cereal and a half a bowl of milk. So to use up the milk, we are forced to pour in more cereal."

He took a deep breath and continued, "Here's the evil part: Cereal companies make their cereal float so that we, the consumer fools, would consume more cereal until we develop liver problems. Thus, the wheels of economy are kept greased."

Luderick went on and on about this, babbling about how envelops and stationery, spaghetti and sauce, pencils and erasers, hot dogs and rolls, holes and the refill dirt never come out even.

After he had calmed down from his larynx-busting tirade, he shut my bedroom door, sat close to me and whispered, "Can you take Ilisha's underwear and give it to me next week?"

I was taken aback but, not wanting to pander to his sexual fantasies so easily, I said, "How much?"

"Five bucks?"

"Five bucks is chump change. I'll be handling my own sister's undergarment. Not exactly my cup of tea."

"OK, Egg. Five bucks and a Penthouse."

This sealed the deal.

The temps dropped to -26°C and became windy after supper. To make matters worse, I had to hike to and from the dungeon after supper in this spit-freezes-before-it-hits-the-ground weather. When I returned Mum and Dad announced they were fed up with the cold weather and we will soon travel to "any place warm." They will meet with a travel agent tomorrow.

Monday, January 17: I missed the 2:55 bus and blew my chance to see the dark-haired girl. A block away from my bus stop, I spied the bus waiting at the red light and ran as fast as my spindly legs could carry me. When I was ten feet from the door, the bus took off! Panting hard and hands on my knees, I watched it puff and belch past me. When I looked up, I saw her! She stood near the back, smiled and waved at me. By the time I raised my hand, I had inhaled enough exhaust fumes to qualify me for a smoky bar in East Vancouver. Damn!

I stopped by the police station to ask about Ilisha's car. The skinny cop shook his head, "Nope, not in. Give it up kid—if we've not found it by now, it's long gone."

Between bites of her dinner chicken, Ilisha announced she scored her fifth straight 100% in trigonometry. How the hell does she manage to play volleyball, date pimply-faced nerds, take five college classes, jog every morning and keep up her grades? She barely studies and whizzes her classes while I, having a social life of a monastic mole with agoraphobia, spend countless hours on schoolwork and yet pull in mediocre grades. My one good subject is English Literature; Mr. Coley always gives me high marks for my weekly free-form essays. However, even though Ilisha has the looks and brains, she sucks at picking the right man. Dweeby is an excellent example.

Speaking of Dweeby, he came to drive her to the volleyball practice. He waited in the entrance while Ilisha put her coat and boots on and I could feel his eyes watching me as I passed by. Creepy.

As I did my homework, Mum and Dad went to the travel agent's office. When they came back, Mum smiled, "Guess what? We're goin' to Florida for four days!"

We'll leave by plane on the night of Wednesday, February 23rd and return on the night of Sunday, February 27th. Ilisha won't be coming because she has study for her midterms coming up in March. So she claims—I smell a big illegal house party coming on. Mice will play when the cats are re-loading their AK-70s.

Tuesday, January 18: While the old Mr. Acipenser droned on in his usual slow, methodical way, I studied the ceiling light and became deeply philosophical. Where does the light go when I turn it off? Does it go back in the bulb? If it doesn't, shouldn't it be bouncing off the walls, getting brighter and brighter until it blinds us? The answer, I surmised, objects absorbs the light, which is why we see them. If they absorb the light after it's turned out, why don't they glow in the dark like the TV does after you've turned it off? Other questions: Is the speed of dark the same as the speed of light? If I use two 50-watt bulbs instead of one 100-watt bulb, will the electricity bill come out the same? Why am I asking these stupid questions?

At 2:45 I burst out the school doors to catch that special bus and rounding a corner, I bounced off Jake's stomach. He picked me off the ground with his bear paws and brought my face close into his.

"Five bucks or five broken fingers, you cripple." His breath stunk of beer. I swallowed and peered around for help. Other students and teachers looked away and kept on walking. Mr. Fry scurried towards the faculty parking lot.

"H-h-here," I trembled as I shoved my hand in my pocket and held out the cash. I'm sure he was happy with the twenty I gave him. I had no smaller bills. I missed the 2:55 bus again.

Homework done, I spent an hour on De Havilland Mosquito model. It's looking good.

Wednesday, January 19: In biology class, Mr. Fry taught us the origins of earth today. When he showed us a short movie, Jake made retching noises during the scenes of volcano eruptions, eeped and ooped monkey sounds and yelled out assorted jokes throughout the film. Everyone laughed but I didn't catch any of the jokes except for the sound effects. The FM system, while it picks up the teacher's voice well, doesn't clearly pick up the students' voices since they're out of the microphone's range.

The teacher didn't even try to reprimand Jake. At 4'7", Mr. Fry, as a biology teacher, is well aware of the nature's creed that big animals eat small animals and he cannot overpower big guys.

In the next period, we had a Latin review test! I didn't know about it until the teacher plunked the test sheet on my desk. I protested and the teacher scolded me, "Egbert, you were not listening. I clearly informed the class yesterday of this test." Damn! I'm sure I failed. At least I pulled a 93% on my philosophy of light essay in Mr. Coley's English Lit class.

I saw the dark-haired girl today! I was on the crowded bus and there she stood, a mere five steps away. As she chatted with two other girls wearing the same uniform, she casually flipped her long dark hair and licked her glossy lips. She glanced in my direction and her eyes met mine across the sea of shoulders. I cracked a smile and felt immediately stupid, because I think I did my happy-monkey-with-a-banana grin.

She smiled back and mouthed, "Hi, how are you?" Her full lips formed each word clearly. I gulped and before I could give a witty Casablanca-style rejoinder, the bus slammed to a stop. My arms flailing, I grabbed a pole that shockingly moved with me and I bounced off an old lady before I rammed my groin into the fare box. In one motion, I stumbled onto the lower step, slammed against the door and made a face print on the door window. The bus was still and motionless as I peeled my cheek from the glass and looked at the driver. Not a sound could be heard. My hearing aid whistled.

"Uh, uh, this is my stop," I croaked.

The driver sighed with contempt, cranked the door open and I floundered out into the cold winds. I dared not look up, for the fear of seeing the dark-haired girl looking down on me. As the bus roared away, I saw what made me perform such a spectacular exit: in my hand was a blind person's walking stick. I checked left and right to see if no one was looking, leaned it against a stop sign and took the next bus home.

While memorizing Mr. Ray's math formulas, Ilisha barged into my room without knocking and slammed her hand on my desk. I jumped.

"Egg, I want my car back! My boyfriend's car broke down on the country road and we had to walk 12 kilometres to the damn garage to have it towed. You keep putting it off—do something!" she fumed before storming out. I'll check the cop's station tomorrow after school. It better be there or else she will soon slip me a drink secretly mixed with sleeping pills and laxatives.

Thursday, January 20: Cripes, if yesterday's bus incident wasn't enough, today was another doozy. Mr. Fry asked me to read out loud a passage on octopus physiology from our textbook: "The octopus is an invertebrate organism with eight tentacles..." When I read this, the whole class burst out in laughter, including Mr. Fry, who knows better not to laugh in these hallowed halls.

"'Tentacles', Egg," he pronounced. "Not 'testicles.' And, 'organism', not 'orgasm.' There are no animals with eight testicles and if there is, he would have a helluva orgasm!" The class roared again in laughter. My face and ears felt hot and I could feel smoke rising from my hearing aids. If the fire alarm went off, it would've been perfect complement to my total embarrassment.

One of the many problems about being hearing impaired is that I'm always the last person to learn the latest gossip. Most hearing people are able to catch stories, jokes and rumours by simple eavesdropping. When something new and exciting makes rounds in small cliques, we hearing impaired folks often have the same confused facial expression of someone sitting in an astrophysics conference when he supposed to be given Flamenco dancing lessons. We look around in vague confusion, our heads swiveling about, a satellite dish trying to receive information we desperately want but are on the wrong channel.

At lunch, my classmates were jabbering and making jokes about something that happened on a bus yesterday. I fine-tuned my satellite dish but I was still lost in a snowstorm of words.

"Hey, what are they talking about?" I asked Bill Bream next to me.

"Someone from our school stole a walking stick for the blind and we're trying figure out who did it."

"Maybe it was Jake, he once stole my hearing aids, ya know," I guessed nonchalantly.

"Nah—it was a smaller kid."

I stopped by the police station on my way home and this time it was different. Good news: Ilisha's car was found three days ago (yes!). Bad news: it was towed away and crushed (someone hand me a Chinese suicide sword).

What to do? I hit upon an idea and stealthily removed a credit card from Mum's purse and driver's licence from Dad's wallet in the kitchen. I left home "visiting Luderick" and took the bus to the car rental agency near the Dorval airport where Billy Bream works part-time after school. He told me the other day that his father owns the place. I explained my predicament and he was cool about it all. He found the same car as Ilisha's and looked the other way when he processed Mum's credit card and Dad's driving licence. I had an awful sinking feeling as I forged Mum's signature on the forms.

"Enjoy the car, Mr. Flounder," he said as he slapped my back and handed me the keys. I don't think I will.

This is getting worse and worse. My head never felt so heavy as this is a slippery slope as slippery as it could be. I was running on ice filled with marbles while wearing roller skates.

I drove the car carefully, parked it one street away, removed the "Rent-a-heap" sticker, left the key in the ignition and sprinted home before someone else steals it again.

"Hey, Ilisha, I found your car! It's sitting up on St. Louis Street. The bad guy must've dumped it there." She eyeballed me and she and Dad walked over to the next street. She came home with the car and while my parents were happy at this "good" turn of events, Ilisha, on the other hand, put on a fake smile and acted gratified. I didn't like the looks of this.

While doing my math homework, Ilisha burst in (again didn't even knock), poked a pointy finger in my bony chest and whispered sternly, "I don't know what you're doing, buster, you should be grateful I didn't squeal to Mum and Dad about the rental car. How stupid do you think I am? Did you think you could pass the car off as mine? The licence plate is different!"

Oops. I don't know what the hell I'm doing or what I'll do next, but I need to think of something fast before the rental charges saddles me with a lifetime of debt no amount of lawn mowing will make up.

Friday, January 21: On the way to the showers after gym, Bill Bream heartily slapped my back and said, "Hey Egg, enjoying the car? Don't take it on highway 20, the cops there won't like to looks of your learner's permit. Ha ha ha!"

Alfonsino jogged up to me at lunchtime, his blue puffy shirt bellowing behind him, "Hey Egg, I heard you got wheels, is it a real chick-mobile, eh? How 'bout we go grocery shopping for women on St. Catherine's street, eh? I'm sure we'll find some mucho big mangos, sweet buns and wet oysters lining up to ride with us." This was accompanied by rude gestures that needed no explanation.

"Sorry Alfonsino, the car is for my sister."

"Oh? Any chance of me scoring a date with her?"

"Forget it, man. She's ugly as a blind carpenter's thumb." I waved him off, not wanting another slobbering guy running after Ilisha.

While we are sitting around eating dinner, Mum spoke up, "I heard from Mora that a gawd-awful teenager stole this blind lady's walkin' stick! She was jest sittin' there on this bus and he swiped it from her hands and took off! It's like a bully stealin' Egg's hearing aids. Who would do such a thing?"

"It's probable the subject has repressed issues surrounding disabilities in regards to his inadequacies," Dad said as he wiped his mouth, "which was expressed in a maladaptive transference from the self to a projected substitute when the opportunity presented itself."

Ilisha piped up, "It was probably a deviate who'll use the stick to beat a little dog."

"That's 'orrible!" Mum gasped.

I looked down and stuffed more corn in my mouth.

Saturday, January 22: Mrs. Taugtog and I practised pronouncing "organism" and "tentacles" without sounding like a Richard Pryer monologue. When I told her how I originally pronounced these words and the teacher's reaction, she pursed her wrinkled lips and said, "No one should make fun of how you mispronounce words, but if you had practised these offending words before, this wouldn't have happened."

After my mouth workout, I went to the dungeon to do my body workout. When I came back from a sweating good session, I examined myself in the big mirror in my bedroom— progress! My chest and shoulders have a hint of a muscle bump. However, my arms are still thin as two sticks for rubbing together to make fire.

Sunday, January 23: With Ilisha in the shower, I stole her black panties from her dresser, sprinted to Luderick's house and made our business transaction. I'm five dollars richer and a new owner of a Penthouse mag. Seeing my good faith in the delivery of the product, we made another business deal. Luderick ordered a pair of Ilisha's bra for $15. I promised him I would deliver the merchandise in one week's time.

Business aside, we played street hockey until Mr. Bullhead threatened to send us to a liver processing plant in Pakistan if the ball ricocheted off his car one more time. We shuffled back inside for a cup of hot chocolate. Luderick's mother was in her prayer room several hours earlier than her usual time.

"She came home late and missed her prayer time last night, so she's doing it now," Luderick explained, his eyes rolling. "In her mind she's on time for her appointment with God, she's praying from the Taiwanese time zone."

We talked in the basement for the better part of a lazy Sunday afternoon and he told about secret government agencies such as:

- Department of Redundancy Department
- Ministry of flat sandwiches
- Department of Departments and Departments
- Department of price stickers that rip off in tiny pieces

This was more interesting than his discussion about sheep that were bred to have shorter legs on one side than the other so they can travel horizontally across slopes. (I commented at the time, "What if they wanted to walk the opposite way? And with shorter legs on one side, the poor sheep would be circling the hill in the same direction all the time!")

On my way home, I talked to a girl who lived down the street. I vaguely knew her and even though she has a personality of a cold fish and a distracting overbite which made lip reading difficult, I enjoyed chatting with her. My heart sank when she mentioned the dreaded words, "my boyfriend." I consoled myself by working on the De Havilland Mosquito model. So far, I'm finished with the body and have attached the wings to it.

Ilisha arrived home as I ate my nightly peanut butter and banana sandwich snack. The flower clock on the wall read 10:37 p.m.

"Guess where I and my boyfriend went with your rental car this weekend?" She grinned with malice. "Quebec City."

Quebec city! Damn—this is about 300 kilometres each way and it will cost me 50 cents a kilometre!

Monday, January 24: With the love part of my brain having a short memory, I decided to try again to take the 2:55 bus to see the dark-haired girl. When I didn't see her on board, I stepped off at the next stop and waited 23 minutes for the next bus while trying to nonchalantly ignore Jake's attempts to hold up a group of construction workers with a water pistol in his coat pocket. No girl.

As soon as I arrived home, Mum rushed breathlessly towards me and exclaimed, "The police cawled. They caught the guy who stole Ilisha's car. You hafta to go to the station to identify the man."

Uh-oh. This problem has turned for the worse. Mum drove me to the police station and they made me look through a one-way mirror at a guy sitting at a small table. I gaped—the dishevelled guy with the bright green parka! The same guy I saw on the bus on New Year's Eve! This time he looked unhappy.

"Uh, that's him," I squeaked. I couldn't believe I did this.

Mum drove me home in silence and she went straight to the kitchen to prepare a big supper. We ate with four of Dad's colleagues tonight. Being in the presence of a tableful of psychiatrists, including my Dad, I felt compelled to ask them a question of psychological matter that has been on my mind for a while.

"I have a professional question to ask you," I paused. "If a car is a phallic symbol, are the fuzzy dice the testicles?" The table erupted with raucous laughter with much pounding on the table. One man burst out with a funny quip in between guffaws and more laughter burst out. The guy sitting next to Dad retorted and another round of chortling exploded.

"What did he say?" I asked Ilisha.

"Oh—you had to be there," she murmured.

"It loses its impact with repetition," Dad explicated.

"It was th' way he said it," Mum's excuse went.

One guy repeated the joke and everyone laughed again. It was still unclear—he sat at the far side of the table and the tall peppershaker covered part of his face so I couldn't read his lips properly. I faked a laugh along with everyone else, maybe a little too loud.

During dessert, the psychiatrist next to me talked to me about his specialty of enlarging women's breasts through hypnosis ("Mammo-hypnotherapist" read his title on the card). Was it an interesting conversation? I don't know. For the life of me I couldn't understand a single word he said because he had a big beard covering his mouth and had a thick Swedish accent. I nodded a lot and parroted the approximation of the sounds of last two or three mumbles he said. I assumed the mumbles stood for real words. I threw in a few "Oh yes, yes", "Really?" to any phrase which remotely might need such a rejoinder. Since these are tricks I've used many times as an experienced hearing impaired person, I don't think he suspected my lack of comprehension at all. I'm able to fool anyone into thinking I understood every word, even if he was a half-blind Azerbaijan astrophysics professor talking to a lamp.

As he droned on and on, I hoped he wouldn't ask me any questions that would give me away. If the person does ask me a question, I throw caution in the wind and say "Yes," and hope I didn't volunteer myself to any vivisection experiments. Luckily, the mammo-hypnotherapist was too busy babbling to ask me any questions. Dad told me the guy later remarked that I was the best conversationalist he's ever met!

After dessert, Dad and his colleagues went into the den to discuss the 1977 classic book, "*Classification of sounds produced by a leather sofa on a hot day*." It came complete with taped sound effects.

I took this moment to ask Mum what the man said about breast enlargement techniques and she, red-faced, brushed my inquiry aside and mysteriously quoted a well-known phrase, "Don't look at a gift horse in the wrong end."

Tuesday, January 25: This morning Jake tormented Mr. Fry by making secret noises during his lecture. They're called "secret noises" because Jake would wait until the professor turned his back to the class to bleat, fart, or moo. Since the culprit cannot be caught in action, it's a perfect crime.

"Who made that noise?" Mr. Fry would ask.

No one dared to finger Jake. The more noises he made, the more agitated Mr. Fry became. It wasn't a pretty sight, seeing a distressed small professor stumbling, stammering and spraying us with his spittle whenever he said, "Seagulls soaring over the isthmus by the seas."

I hope I never practise this last sentence with Mrs. Tautog—too many Ss.

When I arrived at the bus stop after school, I whapped my forehead—I forgot my bus pass in my locker! Damn! Determined to take the 2:55 bus in the name of love, I managed to scrape together 60 cents rattling around the bottom of my schoolbag but I was still 15 cents short. I paid my fare under the bus driver's piercing eagle eyes and strolled past him. His hand shot out, grabbed my bag and dragged me back. He stared at my nickels in the fare box for an eternity and glowered at me, his screwdriver eyeballs boring into my balsam-wood mind. The whole busload of people was giving me the stink eye. I didn't breathe for a good two minutes. He finally released his vice grip and miraculously motioned me on. My exhale was enough to fog up the windows.

I scanned the crowd and jackpot! The dark-haired girl was on the bus! There she was, sitting in the far back with two friends. I sat in one of those elongated seats along the side. My hands trembled and my heart pounded. I stole glances at her as she jabbered and giggled with her two friends. She hardly glanced my way, paying as much attention to me as you would to the demoted plaid sofa in your grandmother's basement. The bus began to fill up in the back with standees and I could see her through a slit between people that would oh-so-briefly flit open as the bus bounced its way down St. Jacques Street.

Before long, I smelled it—cigarette smoke! My newfound girl was illegally smoking on the bus! I spied her and her friends huddling down in the corner as puffs of smoke rose from behind the seat. She must've been perfectly aware of the $500 fine for smoking on public transit; the yellow warning stickers on the windows are there for all to see. The bus violently pulled over and jerked to a stop and several heads swivelled and craned towards the front. There was a startling sight of the angry bus driver shoving his way through people and yelling something in French. The dark-haired girl and her friends frantically put out their cigarettes and swished the smoke away with their hands. The eagle bus driver stopped in front of me, a towering broad-shouldered figure in blue and boomed something in French. The bus became silent as a monastery with its pipe organs at the repair shop. I could smell his cheap musk cologne and see the details of his bus belt buckle. My face felt hot, my throat Sahara desert-dry.

"Je, je ne parle pas français", I stammered. He repeated his question in heavily accented English, his thin lips flopping. This still didn't help—the only word I caught was "You" because it was accompanied by his finger jabbing my chest. Resorting my usual reliable hearing impaired-guesswork, I confidentially replied, "Oui."

Wrong answer.

Before I knew it, my head spun and I was shoved out of the bus and found myself kissing the sidewalk with my butt in the air with a firmly marked shoe print. My school bag sat high on the snow bank above me. The bus roared away, spewing exhaust into my young teenage lungs. I trudged 15 blocks back to school in blowing snow to retrieve my bus pass and arrived home two hours later than I normally do.

I skipped the trek to the dungeon—I couldn't finish my homework on time. I can feel my progress in muscle development melting away, an ice cream cone on hot pavement. My metaphors need work as well.

To my dismay, Ilisha drove the rented car downtown after dinner. What am I going to do about the car? The next trip she will take is drive it to Carp, Ontario and I will jump screaming in front of a snowplow.

Wednesday, January 26: I searched for the appearance of a certain girl on the bus after school—no luck.

Ilisha's boyfriend Dweeby came by to pick her up and waited in the living room while she took forever to get ready. Her C and W song, "Mama get the hammer (there is a fly on papa's head)," was played upstairs at a volume that would peel paint. I was in the dining room, trying to do my homework while dodging falling plaster. Dweeby sat upright and rigid in the hard chair under the lamp, his face a pimply and cratered moon. He picked at his nails and glanced at me from the corner of his eyes. Every time I caught him staring (we hearing impaired people have excellent peripheral vision), he would look away, his face blushing. Did Ilisha tell him I'm handicapped? Was he gawping at me as if I'm Eargor the hearing impaired drooling and lurching about the room?

I decided against going upstairs to my room which would have put me one wall away from Stompin' Tom Conners set at top volume and have my butt massaged and pencils trembling off my desk. I stayed put, switched my hearing aids off and kept my eyes riveted to my Latin homework. Inhibeo means to hold in. Aqua—water. Repugno—to oppose. I finally felt the music shut off.

Ilisha tapped me on the shoulder and I turned my hearing aids back on. "Hey Egg, what are you doing to do about my missing car? I can't keep riding in Mahseer's car all the time, I want my car back or there will be hell to pay," she threatened. Ah, Dweeby's real name is Mahseer. I shrugged and she went out the door with him, leaving an overly relieved schoolboy in the dining room.

Thursday, January 27: I returned to the dungeon tonight and gave my body a brutal workout since I missed Tuesday's session. I half expected my muscles to come bursting out through the skin, but when I looked in the mirror in my bedroom, I still saw a skeleton of a boy. I'm light-years away from my image of the burly Canadian lumberjack. You know the stick figure people draw when they can't properly draw a person? Well, this is me, with hearing aids weighing down my floppy (and muscle-free) ears.

Saturday, January 29: When I looked out the window this morning, I was greeted with a shocking sight that will put a new spin to the stolen car saga. A police car was parked in front with two red Hondas in our driveway! One was the rented car and the other was Ilisha's with nary a dent or scratch.

"What's her car doing here? It was supposed to resemble a crushed beer can." I said to myself. With a mystified frown deep enough to touch my nose, I went downstairs to see Ilisha in the living room talking to the skinny cop. Mum and Dad were not around. My sister and the policeman glared at me. I was a rabbit caught in bright headlights of an onrushing truck.

"Come here," the cop ordered, motioning me over with his hand.

Thoughts of moving to a country where sheep and cows shrink in the rain came to mind.

"We found your sister's car. It wasn't crushed. You were given information about the wrong car."

"Then whose car was destroyed?" I asked.

"It belonged to some dishevelled guy in a bright green parka, the same guy you witnessed stealing her car. We released him this morning."

Oh boy. The amount of guilt I felt was enough to convict a small Istanbul army for removing the tag off mattresses.

They found Ilisha's car aboard a ship heading for Europe along with many other stolen cars after they stopped the captain for having broken regulation lights. After the cop left, I begged Ilisha not to breathe a word to Mum and Dad.

"Okay, but you'll owe me big time, little brother," she said.

I returned the rental and luck would have it, Billy Bream was there. The final bill? $1037.49. There are small countries with less debt! How am I going to pay for this? My bank account never graduated beyond the two-digit amount.

"You better watch the mail box and pay the credit bill before your mother sees it," Billy Bream wisely advised.

Mrs. Tautog made me practise words with the letter "S" ("Seeing a distressed small professor stumbling, stammering and spraying us with his spittle whenever he said, 'Seagulls soaring over the isthmus by the seas.'").

As I write this, a huge snowstorm is raging outside. Damn—I'll have to shovel all the crap off our driveway tomorrow morning.

Sunday, January 30: After two hours of heaving mounds of snow off our driveway, I stole Ilisha's bra from the hamper, stuffed it in a bag and waded through snow to Luderick's house. I saw his and his mother's footprints in the deep snow leading to and from the church to his doorstep. Poor sap. Since the snow was too deep to play street hockey, we stayed inside and played table hockey. I won the 45-minute match 14–9. Luderick suffered from indigestion brought about by an over-consumption of chips and went to the bathroom with a volume from Encyclopaedia Britannica. While I was waiting for him in the kitchen, his pious mother floated in.

"Oh god, have mercy on me," I thought when she settled in the chair across from me.

"Egbert, praise the LORD, God almighty," she waved her arms as if to part the red sea in her sink. "I'll pray for you to become hearing again. JESUS prayed and by the power of the Son of GOD, he made the cripple walk, gave sight to the blind and granted hearing to the deaf. Hail MARY full of grace..." She prayed and pontificated for a good long while about God, Jesus and Mary until Luderick rescued me, numb and eyes glazed over.

Out of earshot, Luderick quipped, "Jesus saves sinners and redeems them for cash and valuable prizes."

We went into the basement to watch a soft-core X-rated videotape he found in an alley downtown yesterday. The picture was horrible—too fuzzy and snowy to see anything worthwhile. We could only hear sound effects and moaning. At one point, his mom yelled something from upstairs and he yelled back, "We're watching a cooking show!" He leaned over to the TV and lowered the volume.

Before I left, I slipped the bag with Ilisha's panties out of my Bomber jacket into Luderick's hands. He shoved it up his T-shirt, paid me and made another business order.

"Hey, can you get me your sister's stockings? I'm gonna fix my mom's car and she needs a new fan belt. Eight bucks."

Smelling a money-inflating deal, I refused at first.

"Ah, come on, Egg. Eight bucks and a nude poster of Samantha Fox."

"Nope, not enough."

We haggled for the next ten minutes and the final deal was $11.50, a nude poster, his grandfather's vintage airplane magazine for a pair of stockings and a photo of Ilisha in a bikini.

Monday, January 31: I met and talked with the dark-haired girl today! As I waited to take the bus home, she came out of the corner *dépanneur* with a new pack of cigarettes. She wore the usual fur coat over her school uniform.

"Hi, how have you been?" she said as she lit a cigarette.

"F-f-fine." I gave her such a big goofy smile that my cheeks must've been touching my ears. She brushed her long thick hair aside, took out a lipstick from her little black purse and proceeded to apply it on her sensuous lips. She muttered something under her breath but her face was turned away from me. I said nothing. My knees trembled and my stomach quivered. I couldn't believe she was there, standing before me and talking to me. Up that moment, she was a distant figure, a famous TV person you see on the street, removed from my sphere of existence but living in my space and time. She said the mumble-words again, her thick hair half-on, half-off her face. My mind was blank.

She said the mumble-words again for the third time while taking a puff of her cigarette, the smoke obscuring her red lips. The only thing that came out of my mouth was my cheese puff breath.

"How come you didn't come to the party at White's bar on New Year's?" This time she faced me and her lips formed the words better. I was impressed with her patience because most people would've backed away and look at me as if I was stoned.

Damn! I went to the wrong bar! I was at Queen's bar.

"Uh, I was invited to another party." Yeah, a pity party.

"What's your name again?"

"Egbert, my friends call me Egg," I rasped. I was sure I've told her my name before.

She extended her hand, "Nice to meet you again, Egg, I'm Molly." Her hand felt warm and soft.

"I wanted to thank you for the job on the bus the other day," She said and added something about the bus driver sprinkled with rude words.

"See you around," she winked and strutted away in her black high-heeled boots. She disappeared around the corner.

I mulled over my head-slapping .50-calibre mistake: How did the hell did I hear Molly say, "Queen's bar" when she really said, "White's bar"? I studied at my lips in the mirror and repeated the words. Queen. White. Queen. White. They look the same on the lips! I blew my chance and I should've double-checked I heard right. But wait, now I think of it—what if her name is "Polly", not "Molly? Nah, I'm sure I heard the "M" sound.

I finally finished the De Havilland Mosquito model, taking longer than usual because I daydreamed about Molly. The last bit painting of the camouflage took ages. Not the best job I've done, a bit of glue have oozed out and dried up on one fuselage and a decal was crooked. I hung it up over my desk.

February

Tuesday February 1st: As I waited for the bus, I looked around for Molly up and down the street and in the *dépanneur* until the counter guy told me to get lost. When she wasn't on the 2:55 bus, I disembarked and I waited 20 minutes in -19 °C bitter cold for the next bus but she was nowhere to be seen. I lost feeling in my toes by the time the bus arrived—this is probably what they meant by "Love hurts."

I dejectedly rode the bus to the Dorval terminus to transfer to the next bus (I take two busses home). Approaching the #202 bus stop, I saw Dweeby waiting for the #211 bus nearby. He stood there, stock straight and still wearing one of those big Russian furry hats with earflaps. He held his briefcase tightly in front of him with both red mitts as if someone would be tempted to steal his day-old peanut butter and jam sandwich inside. He knew I was nearby because he kept glancing in my direction. I ignored him and didn't bother saying anything to him, knowing my queries would've been met with his version of mumble gibberish.

Why does he gawk at me as if I'm a freakish exhibit? Has he ever seen a hearing impaired person before? Maybe not one related to skinny broomsticks. Thankfully, my bus came soon enough to take me away from the creepy geek.

Wednesday, February 2: Last night, I snuck past my parents' bedroom at two in the morning to watch an old black-and-white war movie on TV in the basement. It had several great aerial combat scenes to keep me awake through boring talking head scenes. The 15-minute edge-of-the-seat-mouth-agape-and-not-blinking fight scene between the P-51D Mustang and Luftwaffe Messerschmitt fighter was the greatest. I didn't channel-surf at all even during the boring babble parts because I didn't want to miss the sight of the B-25 flying through the high clouds.

Before I fell asleep, I fantasized me standing on the tarmac by my Spitfire, zipping up my R.C.A.F. jacket, getting ready to fly on a dangerous mission and Molly saying goodbye and pleading me to be careful and come back alive.

"I'll always be in your heart even when I'm in the air," I whispered in her ear before we kissed. However, she was different in my fantasy—a non-smoker and someone who faced me when she pleaded. I wouldn't want to kiss an ashtray.

No Molly today. When will I see her again?

Dweeby came over after dinner and waited in the living room for Ilisha to arrive home from her volleyball practice. I sat in the dining room, doing my math equations. He sat in the hard wood chair with his head bent down, pretending to be absorbed with his fingernails as if he saw them for the first time. From the corner of my eyes I could see he was stealing glances at me. Perturbed, I collected my books and started for my room upstairs. As I passed by, he looked up at me and mumbled something that sounded like a question.

"What?" I asked.

More mumble.

"Sorry, say that again please?"

The same mumbling again.

"Ok, whatever," I shot a guess in the wind to his murky question. He smiled.

"Excuse me, I'm going do my homework in my room." I said before bounding up the stairs at a speed that never will be matched by Canada Post.

Thursday, February 3: I had the most awful experience last night! As I drifted off to dreamland, my bed began to shift, as if it was caving in. I felt the blanket tightening as a heavy weight pressed down next to me and vaguely sensed a warm breeze puffing against the back of my neck. Half asleep, I turned on my light, squinted over my shoulder and to my utter shock, I saw a pizza staring at me! Dweeby! I jerked away, yelled and slammed my elbow up his honker. His head whipped back and he tumbled off the bed. In the shadows, I saw him pick himself off the floor, gripping his nose with one hand and pulling up his pants with his other and lurched out the door. My heart shook and my knees pounded. Before my body could correct its identity confusion, I jumped out of bed and pushed my desk against the door. It took me until 1:30 a.m. for my heart to stop beating enough for me to doze off again.

I wonder if Ilisha knows that Dweeby is gay or simply has affection for skinny, hearing aid wearing boys who speak with a funny accent. I have to do something to make Ilisha break off with pizza face before he tries something worse, like sending me flowers. I've nothing against gays, I accept them for who they are but don't accept them jumping in my bed and scaring the bejesus outta me.

Friday, February 4: For the past few days, I've been searching high and low for Molly on the bus without success. I did see the eagle bus driver, glaring at me as I boarded his bus. I never had so much pleasure showing him my bus pass.

"See? No nickels this time," I chortled in my mind.

Gym day today. Mr. Barracuda, wallowing in his my-goldfish-died-and-my-grandmother-was-arrested-for-indecent-exposure angst, changed the sport. I had dearly hoped we wouldn't play lacrosse again and my prayers were answered! As luck would have it, we had wrestling. This proves that a benevolent God is only around long enough to make sure you don't buy penguins when your mother is not looking. At least wrestling is a change of pace; instead of getting smeared against the gym wall, we are smeared on the gym mat. I now know what a road kill feels after being squished.

"Look alive, men! This is a tough manly sport that will put hair on your chests," Mr. Barracuda bellowed.

I never understood how being miserable and in pain would grow hair. What chest hair? My chest is the ocean and my nipples are two islands and all the hair swam to the islands to avoid hair-eating sharks.

I checked the mail and the credit card bill for the car rental finally arrived. Damn, I owe $3 532.67! It was for the car rental plus other charges my parents made. At least I could pay the $20.00 "Minimum payment" part. I hid the bill in my desk until, somehow, somewhere, the money magically appears. I'm so mad at Ilisha, with all her inane driving around on my dime. Hey—it was not my damn fault her car was stolen in the first place. I struck upon an idea to get back at her. Knowing she takes long showers in the morning that causes half of the population in Dorval to have no water to wash their faces with, I covered the tub bottom with vegetable oil. It's deadly slippery, can't be seen and is approved by vegetarians.

Mum came home late from a job interview in Laval and missed supper. I ate leftover zucchini casserole while Dad told me a story about a patient with paranoid schizophrenia and multiple personality disorder. It was interesting to hear Dad's description of how the patient's seventh personality thought his third personality was after him—the poor guy ran around in circles.

Dweeby didn't come over tonight. Whew! I'm not finished installing the lock on my bedroom door.

The Montreal Canadiens whipped the Hartford Whalers 9–2. I missed watching the game because Mum wanted to watch "*Instructional painting by numbers for the colour blind.*"

Saturday, February 5: Late last night, Dad had to be taken to the hospital after his foot went through the shower stall wall. Mum was sleeping at the time and was awakened by a loud crash followed by a torrent of British curse words to see the foot belonging to aforementioned irate Brit sticking out next to the dresser.

Dad was at the breakfast table sporting a small cast on his ankle, looking annoyed. He demanded Mum to "buy one those bloody suction-cup mats for the tub." He has to hobble around on crutches for the next several weeks. Good idea I had to wash the tub out before everyone woke up.

I read a newspaper item in the *Montreal Star* reporting that the Rasbora cult is trying to recruit more members and several irate parents are demanding for the arrest of the cult's leader after their sons and daughters have disappeared into the group's clutches. Apparently, they prey on young, confused university freshmen because they're easy targets. Mum saw me reading the article and cryptically said, "Never wear a striped shirt around near-sighted zebra hunters."

After a lip-flapping session with Mrs. Tautog, I went to the dungeon and had a so-so workout. I stopped by Luderick's house on my way home and sold him my promised merchandise (Ilisha's stockings) and professionally gave him a bill of sale.

"Hey, Egg, I want to order Ilisha's lipstick and eye shadow, he whispered, even though his mother wasn't home. His mother had gone to a special church sermon to listen to the reverend's topic on greed. A game of bingo was to follow.

"Okay Luderick, that's gonna cost ya. Ten bucks and your new hockey stick."

"Deal!" he eagerly shouted, maybe a little too loud.

To get Luderick off this icky topic, I told him about what happened the other night with Dweeby and do you want to know what he said? "Does this mean you're not a virgin anymore?" Jeez! He promised not to tell his small-minded mother, who thinks homosexuals would be better used as emergency organ donors or speed bumps.

For a solid two hours, we brainstormed a way to break Ilisha and Dweeby up. Mum's strange comment and the coming of the Rasbora cult gave us an idea to work with. Luderick has vested interest since he wants to catch Ilisha on the rebound, "Preferably with a bottle of wine and a vibrating bed." In the end, we thought of a plan that has a reasonable chance of working. It'll be called "Operation Breakup."

Tomorrow is an important day—my birthday! I hope hope hope to get the F-14 Tomcat model I had been hinting for.

Sunday, February 6: Exactly seventeen years ago today, I arrived to our wonderful, confusing world in a clean white delivery room where the doctor, holding me upside-side down by my little feet, had to slap the nurse to keep her from laughing. Another important point about this birthday: it's my last year of being a teenager. In one more year, I'll be deemed an "adult."

So I thought.

"Egg, you still have two more teenage years to go 'cause eighteen n' nineteen are still 'teen' numbers, never mind what th' surgeon general says," Mum explained.

I have to wait two more years! It's like being five inches from the finish line and having another mile to run.

We had the usual festivities at home—cake, presents and cheerful calls from relatives, all translated by Mum. Luderick was there with us under psychiatrist Dad's watchful eye. He was happy to skip evening church mass for my party. Dweeby arrived for the dessert which was a cake resembling a porcupine with long thin candles covering it.

"Mum, I'm too old for animal cakes!" I freaked. Ilisha laughed and Luderick ogled at her jiggling chest. I kicked him under the table.

Mum said, "You must keep yer childhood 'cause you have one chance to be a child. You will be spendin' 'bout 55 years as an adult, if you live to be 75."

Dad agreed, rubbing the cast on his foot, "For the rest of your life my dear lad, you'll be pining for the good ol' days of childhood when you didn't have to pay bloody taxes, suffer from hemorrhoids or have hair growing in strange places."

But I already have hair growing in strange places.

Speaking of strange hair, what's the real purpose of pubic hair? If it's there to protect my family jewels from friction incurred during acts of love as they say, therefore I should've more hair on the soles of my feet. Take a gander at these figures. The number of times I use my feet per day: thousands. The number of times I've boinked in my lifetime: zero. Following this logic, a male porn star should look like Fozzie bear from the waist down.

Looking at the presents I received this year made me understand why birthdays are no longer as exciting as they used to be. I got an electric shaver (my father was optimistic, it's as useful as an exercise tape for the dead), a total of 110 dollars from assorted relatives and a lime-green T-shirt with a pair of bright purple corduroy pants from Mum (who has the same sense of colour coordination as a 67-year-old golfer). I can see the T-shirt being used as a car rag in the future. Luderick gave me dark sunglasses.

"Your earpieces, a nifty black suit and you'll be a real secret service man." Good for looking cool while bumping into telephone poles.

Then the mother of all gifts: Dweeby's. First, I opened the card stuck on the gift. In the envelope were ten shares of a "Microsoft" company. He mumbled something as I turned the paper over in my hands. Ilisha spied my blank look and translated, "He says it's a new computer company that will be big someday, only employees have these stocks and they're not available for the public yet." They'll be good for scrap paper for my math homework. The kicker was his gift. I tore apart the turquoise cellophane wrapper and pulled out the item out of the box. The table fell dead silent—it was a gold-framed picture of him wearing a purple satin bathrobe.

"Uh, thanks, I think this is for Ilisha," I said as I handed the picture to my bewildered sister. Dad frowned and Luderick sniggered. Man—I can't wait to initiate "Operation Breakup" tomorrow.

Ilisha had the presence of mind to buy me a great gift: a metallic model of a Grumman F6F Hellcat jet with a stand to put on the corner of my desk. Other than this, no F-14 Tomcat model, no airplane posters, no other gifts related to planes. I'll use the birthday money for real presents.

In preparation for "Operation Breakup," I made a necklace of margarine lids and cut a white robe out of old bed sheets. While I strung the necklace together, I thought of something interesting: If I were to live to be 135 in the year 2101, which is possible if I keep off the potato chips, I would've lived through 13 decades, three centuries (20th, 21st and 22nd) and two millenniums. If this happens, what changes would I see? What great world events would've happened? This gave me an idea for an essay for English Literature class and I wrote a two-page fictional TV interview exchange with a 135-year-old man.

Monday, February 7: We had public speaking class this morning and, to my shock, I learned that my presentation was due today! I thought it was due next week. So, I had to wing it again on the spot. After Jake's speech on the proper method of cleaning a deer carcass, I croaked a bad philosophical argument of how the typical household toaster is constructed to never cook a slice of bread evenly on both sides.

From his usual seat from the corner of the class, Mr. Bonito mumbled something. Billy Bream later told me that he said, "Egg, you need to be better prepared, you were supposed to talk about your favourite hobby not about kitchen appliances. Your mark is 44%."

Tabernac! I don't understand everything the professor says because his huge mustache covers his mouth. This is one of the damning problems about being hearing impaired: I miss crucial announcements in class such as exam dates, assignment deadlines and updates on Jake's latest criminal activity.

Still no Molly. I've not seen her for a week and am becoming discouraged. Did I scare her off? Was it my cheese puff breath?

Upon coming home, I changed into my white shirt and pants and performed the first step of "Operation Breakup" which entailed screwing up enough courage to see Dweeby at his university. Luderick picked me up in his mother's 1973 Pinto and drove to the Malcolm Technical University. Luderick, with a learner's permit so new that it was dated tomorrow, squinted through his mother's hanging rosaries and the line of Mary and Jesus figurines along the dashboard as he crept through rush-hour traffic. The tape cassette played, "I Don't Care If It Rains or Freezes 'long As I Have My Plastic Jesus Sittin' On The Dashboard of My Car." Once downtown, he sped through two red lights, weaved too close to the edge of the bridge and bounced over every possible pothole in Montreal. My lovely finger imprints on the dashboard will stay there for years to come.

Luderick waited in his mother's holy smoking heap in front of the computer sciences building as I went in to search for a certain monosyllabic pizza-face. I found Dweeby working alone in his computer lab and didn't relish the way his eyes lit up like two flashbulbs when he saw me, but it was short-term pain for long-term gain.

"I came here to tell you Ilisha was in a car accident," I said with my best somber face.

"Watermelon!" he gargled loudly (my interpretation of what I heard).

"She's OK and was just released from the hospital. She got hit badly in the back of her head. Seems her visual system is affected."

"Black elastic with pentagon cows?" he queried.

"She can only see things that are white. Everything else is invisible to her. This is why I'm wearing white, or else she will mistake me for a lamp post."

"Ski-doo?" Dweeby exclaimed with wide-eyed astonishment.

Taking the white robe out of my bag, I handed it over to him, "You'll have to wear this every time you see her."

"Whooperill, fort phone book?"

"Yes. Also, you also have to wear this necklace," I said as I gave him the string of margarine lids. "Since the accident has traumatized her, she feels more comfortable around these large lids."

"Okay," Dweeby uttered what was his first properly articulated word I've ever heard.

"Oh yeah, one more thing. You'll need to speak loudly, she lost some hearing."

"Lip."

Tuesday, February 8: This morning, I went ahead with phase II of "Operation Breakup." I caught Ilisha on her way out to her daily morning jog.

"Hey, Ilisha, I saw your boyfriend on my way home. It seems he's hooked up with that Rasbora cult."

"What do you mean?"

"He was wearing this white robe and a necklace of margarine lids the other day the same way they do. He talked in a very loud voice—I could hear him clear across the street."

"What did he say?" she said, gulping hook, line and sinker.

"Dunno. He was chanting loudly, maybe in another language. When are you seeing him next?"

"I want to see it myself. He'll be coming over tomorrow."

For a dose of confusion between two soon-to-be ex-lovers, I want to see this myself, too.

Wednesday, February 9: Woke up 1:30 a.m. with a realization I had forgotten to go to the dungeon last night. I'm starting to lose interest in bodybuilding and my lumberjack image is fading away, a hazy mirage.

Waiting for my bus on this warm winter day, a BMW pulled up next to me at the red light and there, sitting next to an older guy, was Molly. The guy could be her father. Heart fluttering, I was about to knock on the window to greet her but stopped short when I saw the guy lean over and kiss her with his tongue in her mouth. My heart fluttered down with a thud in the salt-stained snow as I watched them drive off. Now I know why she hasn't been taking the bus these days.

I rushed home from school to catch the Dweeby and Ilisha show. With Ilisha waiting downstairs for the newest recruit from the Rasbora cult, I sat by my bedroom window, eating popcorn. Within a few minutes, I saw Dweeby, robes flowing behind him and margarine lids swinging from his neck, walking down one side of the street. Lo and behold, from the opposite direction, a small parade of cult members came marching and, deducing from the synchronous open-close movements of their mouths, chanting. The mid-point between Dweeby and the cult was my sister. He and the group moved closer and closer towards an inevitable confrontation in front of our house. My sister burst forward, ran towards Dweeby and at the same time, the Rasboras spot him, a lost sheep from the herd. I ate my popcorn faster and watch them welcome him with open arms, a poor, confused sheep. Ilisha scuffled with them and much shouting and arm waving ensued between the three parties. The cult members dragged Dweeby away from

Ilisha who yelled at him and used a gesture similar to the "safe" signal ("We're finished! We're finished!"). She stormed back into the house. He was pulled away despite his mumbled protests and frightened backward glances to the door where Ilisha, his now ex-girlfriend, disappeared into.

Yes! The plan worked!

Thursday, February 10: As I waited for the bus on my way home, a large crowd of students from my school and other schools amassed at my stop. I was the first one to get on and I took a window seat in the back. Glancing among the stragglers outside, I spied Molly near the end of the crowd of humanity embarking the bus. Finally! She was digging through her Chanel handbag, her beautiful eyes fraught with worry. She glanced up and we locked eyes and a thrill surge shot up my back. She hissed something to me, words silent through the bus window.

I mouthed, "What?"

She mouthed back in an exaggerated tone and gestulated, "I lost my bus pass, give me yours."

Having used my super lip-reading powers and wanting to save my damsel in distress, I slid the window open and casually dropped my bus pass outside. She picked it up from the snow, looked up and enthused a "Thank you!" which was accompanied by a kiss gesture where her hand touched her chin and not her lips. Close enough for me. I shivered in excitement—she's coming on the bus to see me! I scanned carefully through the crowded bus for Molly's approach and glimpsed her shouldering her way towards me, but she stopped and began to talk to someone sitting five rows up. Craning my neck, I noticed it was an older guy in an expensive ski jacket. She stood over him, smiling and laughing at his jokes. The bastard—he didn't even offer her his seat. I would've given her the whole bus! My stomach roiled as I waited impatiently for her to come to me. Somewhere in Ville Saint Pierre, she and the guy stepped off the bus—with my bus pass, no less! I tried to slide open the window to call out to her but it was frozen shut. Nevertheless, it was odd that it wasn't her usual stop.

Before I stepped off the bus, I asked the driver for a bus transfer and he refused. Damn! I couldn't take the #202 bus home! With no bus pass, no cash and a deflated heart, I plodded home in the -21°C wind-chill factor cold, a long 35-minute trip. As I write this, my toes and fingers are still defrosting.

Friday, February 11: As Mum slept in this morning, I removed bus money from her purse and pangs of guilt rose as I shoved the money in my dress pants. No way in hell I could tell her how I lost my bus pass. Tales of derring-do with Molly will wait until our wedding reception, if this ever happens.

On the way to school, Molly walked on the bus in Ville Saint Pierre with the same guy in the ski jacket she was with yesterday. She noticed me sitting alone and sauntered directly over to me. She stood next to me, fished out my bus pass from her little black purse and handed it to me.

Here's your pass. Did you get home okay?" she said sweetly.

"Uh—no problem," I shrugged as I pushed my school bag off the seat to give her room to sit next to me. She didn't take the hint! She turned to strut to the back to sit with the ski jacket guy. A few minutes later, a smelly old guy took the seat meant for her. For the rest of the ride, she didn't even glance at me all the while they laughed and smiled together. The ugly roiling feeling returned.

In English literature class, Mr. Coley said he enjoyed my piece about the fictional TV interview starring me as a 135-year-old man. He gave me 91%.

We had wrestling again for gym period. I don't know why it's called "wrestling." It doesn't resemble what the Hollywood wrestlers do on television. All we do is make loud grunting noises, squirm around and suffer mat burns with the goal of turning the opponent over to his back. "Turtle flipping" would've been a better name for this sport.

"Hollywood wrestling is fake and what you wieners are doing is the real thing," growled Mr. Barracuda. The one good part about wrestling is its visual aspect. I understand little of what Mr. Barracuda bellows in a gym that echoes so much that my classmates can hear reverberations of the screams from the class before us. I function in gym by watching my classmates and doing exactly what they did after. I observe and make sure I'm not the first guy to try a new move.

Today, Jake broke Todd's arm in two places and from that point on, all his partners learned to flip themselves on their backs and concede defeat as quickly as possible to avoid being the next Cubism model.

As I rode the bus home, I mulled about Molly and decided I don't want to see her face again. Why would she flirt with me while hanging out with another guy?

While watching the hockey game, Ilisha came downstairs and demanded, "Egg, have you seen my black lace bra?"

"You mean the thing Dad uses to scare mice away?"

"Ha ha ha," She mocked.

I've got to be more careful with conducting my business with Luderick. What if I'm caught with her undergarments? How the hell would I explain this?

Saturday, February 12: After Mrs. Tautog's session ("Th, th, th" until my tongue dried up), I worked out in the torture dungeon and on the way home I saw Jake sitting in back of a passing police car. I looked away; he didn't see me and neither did I see the stop sign. I'm sure it's still wobbling as I write this. Rubbing my face, I stopped by Luderick's house for a short visit.

As I stood inside the entrance, I told him what happened with Dweeby and Ilisha the other day and he was overjoyed, a mite too much for me.

"Did she look especially despondent and love-starved afterwards?" was his first question.

"How does one look love-starved?"

"Was she calling out my name in her sleep?"

"People talk in their sleep?"

"Did she ever even mention me?"

"I think she did once, but it had something to do with ten foot poles."

He wasn't a happy camper. I consoled him with Ilisha's lipstick and eye shadow I stole from her purse and made the business exchange. He was happy to fork over ten dollars and his new hockey stick for something that cost me nothing.

As I pulled on my Montreal Canadiens toque on, he made another bold business order: a pair of Ilisha's red high heel shoes for 12 dollars and a pack of nude playing cards.

"No way, man. Ilisha has been sniffing around. It won't be long before I'm busted." Acting out of desperation, he quickly upped the price to 20 dollars. I, shamelessly taking advantage of the situation, refused. We negotiated the business deal to more reasonable terms and agreed on the final price: 25 dollars, nude playing cards and a wrinkled autographed 1975 hockey card of Canadiens goalie Ken Dryden.

With his mom due back from shopping, I left quickly. I noticed a church flyer on the table by the door. It read, "A bean supper will be held on Tuesday evening in the church hall. Music will follow."

The school dance is next week! I live for these dances. Canterbury is an all-boys school and we boys are lonely sailors after a six-month leave. It gets so bad girl-wise that our cafeteria cook, Mrs. Catfish, who has more hair on her mustache than the entire grade sevens put together, is the best looking female in our school. At all dances and other social events, the girls from St. Annabelle's Academy come to our school to party. The population of our school: 600 boys. The population of St. Annabelle's: 2150 girls. This situation may be akin to a rooster in a full henhouse, but it's not. Two facts: 1) teenage boys' hormones are as agitated as 24 psychotics in a rubber room with one Rubik's cube and, 2) girls don't peak sexually until they are in their 40s. The result? Most of the guys in our school go to the dances and a few girls do. This evens out the male-female ratio.

Another good part about these dances is that Jake never goes because his immense size makes girls scatter like seagulls do after a little boy runs through a flock. It's the only time we guys have no need to look over our shoulders and fear the telltale rumble and shadow.

Monday, February 14: Valentine's Day. Something tells me I need a girlfriend if the only females who I can give a Valentine's Day card to are my mother, grandmother and our cat. I wish I had a girlfriend; everyone seems to have one—even Mickey Mouse. No fair.

Friday, February 18: After school, I saw Molly waiting for the BMW guy outside an office building, puffing a cigarette, looking achingly beautiful as ever with fresh red lips and long brown hair cascading down her shoulders. I pulled up my scarf and looked away as I shuffled by. When I glanced back, I saw the guy step out of his car and kiss her. My knees buckled and I stumbled in the deep snow but regained my balance and dared not look again. Damn him—hope he dies of second-hand smoke! And, hey—what about the ski jacket guy?

Dreary news side, the school dance is tomorrow! This is an exciting, happy time! I'm counting the hours instead of days. Alfonsino nudged me as we walked out French class and chortled, "Hey Egg, ready for the babe-o-rama tomorrow? Watch me make my grand entrance—I just found the ultimate babe magnet."

"Are you gonna dress up as a car magnet?"

He frowned at me curiously, his lips pursing.

"You know Alfonsino, we don't want the old bag Mrs. Catfish with her metallic replacement hips come whooshing towards you with her legs open."

Mum's job interview didn't go well this morning and she spent the whole night watching, *"Senior Citizen All-Star Cribbage and Wrestling Competition."*

Saturday, February 19: I spent the afternoon getting ready for the dance, part of it was with Mrs. Tautog practicing my question, "Do you want to dance with me?" without whistling out of my schnoz. I spent most of my time on deciding what to wear. I picked dark wool dress pants and a red collar shirt with short sleeves (red to hopefully stimulate the girls' glands). I made sure my hair covered my hearing aids and used many spritzes of Ilisha's hair spray to keep it in place. I verified my supplies:

- Comb—check.
- Breath mint—check.
- Money—check.
- School I.D.—check.
- Hearing aid batteries—check.
- Backup hearing aid in case one fizzles in the pounding music—check.

For supper, Mum offered me baked beans. I refused, telling her I didn't want to increase the methane content of our atmosphere.

"Mum, the cows and the farmers are doing a good enough job of that out there in Saskatchewan." I rolled my eyes.

I ate two peanut butter and banana sandwiches and eight after-dinner mints to cover up the peanut butter breath. I brushed my teeth twice before Mum drove me to the school gym. We arrived at 7:30 p.m. The Valentine's day-themed dance started at eight o'clock but I wanted to be early to check out my prospects.

About half an hour after I arrived, I saw Alfonsino Troutio strutting onto the dance floor among the heart-shaped balloons, his arms waving about as if he was leading a swimming class for senior citizens. His hair was built into a large pompadour that bounced over his forehead, an Olympic diving board in need of tuning. He wore a white puffy shirt and a large black jacket with padded shoulders ("To give that big, rugged look," he said). The shirt was unbuttoned to the mid-waist to expose his "hairy" chest. I put hairy in quotation marks because what was hair wasn't hair at all. To cover his normally bald pecs, Alfonsino had glued pieces of his mother's old wig onto his chest.

"Mother doesn't need it, she no longer wears it," Alfonsino whispered.

"But Alfonsino," I exclaimed through my teeth. "It looks ridiculously fake."

"Well, if wimmin can have false eyelashes, padded bras and fake nails, we guys can have toupees and fake chest hairs. It's dark enough here—dem chicks can't tell the difference between the real and fake stuff."

"Hey Alfonsino, how are you going to get the hair off at home?"

His eyes widened with blank look. Evidently, he didn't think of this.

During a slow song, I was dancing with a girl and saw Alfonsino and another girl dancing nearby. When the song ended, the girl quickly pulled away and her sweater zipper caught a piece of Alfonsino's chest hair and ripped out a fist-sized piece. In a space of 15 seconds, the skinny Lebanese made several painful facial contortions that would've won him a Jack O'Lantern pumpkin-carving contest. He tried to chase after the girl to get the piece back but lost her in a crowd of giggling girls. Yet, determined to fill his girl quota, Alfonsino ducked into the bathroom and coloured in the bald spot with large black marker before boogying back onto the dance floor.

Overall, it was great evening. I love these dances—I always sleep with soft dreamy memories of holding a warm, sweet-smelling girl close to my heart as we rotate gently to the slow beat of a love song. I'm on cloud nine for nine minutes. The slow songs are my favourite because it's the one time I can hold a girl close without getting arrested for sexual harassment.

However, the connection between our two souls becomes sadly ephemeral, because once the song is over, I don't see her again. My problem is that I'm clueless as to what to do next. What do I do when the song ends? How can I talk to her if the music is too loud and it's too dark to read lips? How can I ask for her phone number if I can't talk to her on the phone? What if her name is Virginia and I mispronounce it?

I often wish I had an older brother advising me how to get a date with the girls I meet at these dances. Having an older sister who regards me as an electronic device for cleaning shoes, I'm left to learn this by myself. I'm a solitary boat sailing uncharted waters without a CSA-approved life jacket.

It's 12:30 a.m. as of this writing and I shall go to bed and have pleasant dreams of the evening.

Sunday, February 20: Woke up this morning feeling a mild melancholy similar to post-Christmas depression. I waited for this dance for two months and it's over.

After doing my homework, I snuck into Illisha's room and lucked into finding her red high-heeled shoes and went to Luderick's house. After letting me in, he dragged me into his room, shut the door and asked, "Well, do you have the merchandise?"

"Yeah—here," I whispered. As soon as I gave Luderick the bag with the shoes, he made a new business order with his mother out of earshot, a big risky one. After a few initial refusals to deliver the merchandise on my part, we negotiated and settled on a deal. The merchandise: Ilisha's red dress ("The low-cut one she wore at last summer's barbecue party at your place."). The price: 50 dollars, his grandfather's WWII RCAF badge and a 1978 Guy Lafleur hockey card. Good enough for me.

We played a new variation of street hockey—one-on-one with an empty net. The object was to prevent the other from scoring while attempting to score ourselves. The game ended in a 0–0 tie because we were wrestling too much in the snow bank while the ball remained forlornly untouched for the most part of the game. We won't try this futile experimentation with street hockey again.

Monday, February 21: I brought home my mid-term report card.

Biology (Mr. Fry)   70%

Instructor comments: Doesn't pay attention as needed; other students easily distract Egbert.

Public speaking (Mr. Bonito)   64%

Instructor comments: Egbert needs to be more organized and prepared. Doesn't follow given presentation topics.

Latin (Mr. Acipenser)   71%

Instructor comments: Not always prepared for quizzes.

Physical education (Mr. Barracuda)   75%

Instructor comments: Shows motivation but needs greater willingness to be involved.

<u>Math</u> (Mr. Ray)   66%

Instructor comments: Inconsistent scores on the weekly quizzes.

<u>English literature</u> (Mr. Coley)   95%

Instructor comments: Creative free-form writing samples, keep up the good work!

<u>French</u> (Mr. Poisson) Oral: 58% Written: 64%

                                        Overall: 61%

Instructor comments: Mr. Flounder needs to improve pronunciation and listening skills.

My average came to 72%, a drop from last term's average of 76%. Mum and Dad's reactions were lukewarm at best. Dad advised, "You can do better than that, my lad. You need to be better prepared for those quizzes."

I packed for our Florida trip the day after tomorrow. I can't wait be on the plane, it'll be my virgin flight. I'm more excited about the prospect of travelling than the destination. Even if we were flying to Winnipeg, I would still be excited. All my life, I've dreamed of being in a cockpit and flying the vast skies. On early Saturday mornings as a young kid, I used to hold a small model plane next to my eye and I became the plane, swooping over the land of bed-sheet mountains and valleys as the dust-flecked sunbeams streamed through the morning window.

Countless times I've stared at my worn and fading WWII posters and felt the control stick in my hands, the rush of air through the dipping wings and the sensation of curving off to the side as I search for wily enemy aircraft. I always watch the planes pass overhead until it disappears into the distance and wonder what it'll be like, up high, sitting by the window and looking down at the land far below. Living close to an airport does have its advantages other than drowning out Ilisha's crappy music. If I hear, "I flushed you from the toilets of my heart" one more time, I'll ralph my mac and cheese supper.

Tuesday, February 22: At school, I heard post-dance news from Bill Bream: Alfonsino had to be taken to the hospital by his beehive hairdo-mother to have his fake chest hair surgically removed. The procedure was a long and labourious one; the doctors had a difficult time removing it because they were laughing too hard.

"And guess what happened next?" Bill Bream grinned. "The surgery left a quarter-sized scar in the middle of his chest—it looks like he has three nipples!" Also, as part of the skin graft procedure, the doctor used the skin from his butt, so he had to stand all day in the back of the class.

According to the regulations drawn up by the school board, Mr. Fry was required to teach human reproduction today. This was something he dearly wanted to avoid, not because of the potential embarrassment of saying "vagina" to a roomful of squirming young boys, but because of Jake. He has been looking forward to this lecture all year long due to its potential for ridicule.

The teacher faced the expectant class, gulped hard and stammered, "Today, um, we will be talking about, um, human sexual reproduction." Jake gave a cheer from the back of the class and stimulated an act normally performed by yourself in a locked bathroom. I'll never look at flossing the same way again. This was only the beginning.

The rest of the class was a string of ribald chortling, shouted questions and rude noises from the big dork. After class, Bill Bream recited Jake's rude questions: "How big is it?" "Can you demonstrate how they do it?" and, "What do you mean when I was born, the doctors tried to push me back in?" Mr. Fry made the lecture as dry and boring as possible, filling it with many medical terms and ambiguous board-drawn diagrams. This didn't deter Jake from interrupting the class every 45 seconds. I, for one, couldn't concentrate on this important lecture and was annoyed by his heckling.

Alfonsino, on the other hand, stood quietly in the back of the class, audiotaped the lecture and took 12 pages of notes with wide-eyed fascination. He even asked Mr. Fry if he could get extra tutoring in this topic after school.

Stepping out of school, I saw Molly and the BMW guy walk hand-in-hand on the far side of the office parking lot. I'm sure it was them; I can recognize her black high-heeled boots and her sauntering walk anywhere. Why am I letting this bother me?

After dinner, I put the last of my clothes in my suitcase and am raring to be flying up in the blue skies tomorrow. Ilisha put on an act at the supper table, saying, "Oh Mum and Dad, I'll miss you. If it weren't for the lousy volleyball games, I would've gone with you." Yeah, and the Toronto Maple Leafs will win the Stanley cup.

I went bodybuilding and grunted a good, hard workout and, before going to bed, I checked my body in the mirror for any sign of muscle. Save for aches and pains, I have no gains to speak of. I don't think I've the body for the Florida beaches yet.

Wednesday, February 23: I flew and we are in Daytona, Florida! Mum and Dad picked me up after school and drove straight to the airport. Since it was my first time boarding a plane, the procedure involved was new to me. When we handed our luggage to the boarding check-in woman, she put a tag on each bag that read, "DAB." I've read that luggage tend to go in the opposite direction from where their owners are flying to and my mind panicked, "Argh! My suitcase will go to 'Dab', a mysterious island where all lost luggage congregate!" All along the beaches, I could see pale-looking luggage lying around drinking leather-tasting beverages and talking about the local baggage strike while trying to turn into a dignified tan colour.

"Dad," I said in my best warning voice. "Our baggage will be going to a place called Dab or Dabra, Indonesia."

He patted my shoulder and said, "Don't worry my lad, they will go to Florida. DAB is a code to tell the baggage people as to which plane to load."

Upon hearing this, I fretted that a dyslexic baggage person will send my suitcase to Africa where, a few months later, I'll see the natives wearing my "Underdog" underwear in a National Geographic TV special.

After the baggage check, we went through the U.S. customs where we showed our passport while being interrogated by a stony-faced border guard. I was careful not to say anything that rhymes with "bomb."

They inspected Dad's crutches and cast on his foot for any hidden weapons by passing a wand detector around it. At least they didn't laugh at his giant blue sock covering it.

One thing that customs officials, policemen and city bus drivers have in common, aside from tired, serious dog faces, is that they all mumble. Little difference could be seen between the lip movements they make while talking and while breathing. I wish enunciation classes were part of their training. They wouldn't have to repeat three times and still be facing a boy with a blank look on his face and think he's stoned.

We waited in the lobby for an hour with many weary people until a loud babble came over the intercom. Like conditioned sheep, everyone lined up, showed their tickets and walked through a neat tunnel attached to the plane's door to step inside the big plane. We waited on the tarmac for a good 30 minutes before the plane began to move out the port. The lift-off was exhilarating! The plane went faster and faster and the rumble became increasingly pronounced and an indescribable stillness filled the air as the heavy plane lifted off. We flew high above our town and I saw our street, the shopping centre and my school far below, all small pieces on a model train set. I even spied Jake breaking a car window. The scene below faded away as we drifted upwards through a massive cloud to a beautiful topside—light blue ceiling, a puffy white floor and an orange setting sun beaming from the far horizon. If I died right there, I would've died happy. Actually no—I wanted to live long enough to experience the landing.

I asked Dad if we have to change our watches to correspond to the new time zone but he said that we are flying in the same latitude and the time was the same. I pondered about the different time zones around earth and thought, "Why not have one standard time throughout the world?" For example, when it's 5:00 p.m., in Greenwich, England, it should be the same time in New York, Tokyo, Vancouver and Moscow—everywhere. This would eliminate the international dateline, time zones and possibly jet lag. Work shifts would be more economic, scientific measurements of time would be more consistent and international appointments wouldn't be missed because of the "My time, your time" confusion.

To pass time so to speak, I read my RCAF history book, ate peanuts, drank pop and watched a boring onboard movie without the sound. The headsets they proffered me were useless against my hearing aids. At around 9:30 p.m., the plane floated down over the lighted city of Daytona, a beautiful, peaceful sight. We picked up our luggage (whew—none were missing) and took a taxi to the hotel. It's incredible that, in a couple of hours' flight, you can go from a -30 °C zone to one that is +20 °C. And no snow!

Dad quipped, "If you miss the snow, my lad, I'll scrape some out of the freezer and pile it on the floor for you to shovel."

Thursday, February 24: Dad woke me up at 6:30 this morning, mouthed in my bleary face, "Get up, my lad, we have loads to do." I stepped outside into the warm morning air and found it hard to believe I'm wearing shorts in February. Normally, if I were dressed like this in Canada, I'd be in gym class playing snow football to the benefit of miserable Mr. Barracuda. I watched the weather report in the hotel lobby. It will be plus 5 °C back home and 28 °C in Florida today.

We ate breakfast in the hotel restaurant and I had a genuine Florida orange. It wasn't anything special—it tasted the same as it does back home. The first attraction we went to was Dolphin World.

It was neat. Dolphin World has seals, killer whales and dolphins jumping through hoops, giving their trainers a ride and doing other things. Dad explained how they trained the animals to do tricks with special reinforcement schedules based on psychological learning principles. It gave me a few ideas of what I can do with Ilisha. Dad didn't enjoy himself much, complained of having to hobble about with the "bloody crutches."

After lunch, we set back out again to drive to the beach. The beach was crowded since this was spring break week for many schools. Dad relaxed in his lawn chair, his crutches by his side and read, "*On Contiguity Relationships Between Events in the Egyptian and Coptic Verbal Systems: How to say 'ah' whilst being examined by a proctologist."* Mum slept on her towel, soaking up the sun's rays.

About the beach itself: Oh man... the WOMEN! I've never been in the presence of so many good-looking college girls. I sat on my towel and ogled at all the sweaty, bouncing women in microscopic bikinis passing by ever so closely, prompting me to pull up my knees to my chest to hide a certain embarrassing growth. The giant pimple on my chest hasn't gone away yet.

As my punishment for doing excessive eye exercises, I'm sun burnt. My back, neck and upper arms are as red as a Baboon's butt. Mum rubbed in a skin ointment, allegedly to "soothe the pain." Mum must've been trained in the School of White Lies, the same school dentists and doctors learn to say, "This won't hurt." She scrubbed in the ointment in the same manner a muscle-bound Russian housekeeper would do to remove red wine from a carpet. This must be her way of exacting revenge for pain incurred while giving birth to me.

Friday, February 25: According to the *"Florida Times"*, it will be sunny and plus 10 °C in Montreal. Dad put down the paper and morosely said, "Bloody hell, just our luck to go to Florida during one of Montreal's rare winter Indian summers."

Mum shrugged, "We'll enjoy what we can, dear, you know the grass is always greener than two in the bush."

Today we went to a museum Dad had always wanted to go. Normally, museums are about as exciting to me as a 1972 Encyclopedia of Filled-in Tax Forms, but this was an interesting one. "History of Oddities: Odd People, Places and Things" humourously examines, with neat exhibits and films, a variety of strange and extraordinary phenomena. Here are the best ones:

- The first woman with nictophobia: the fear of walking backwards into a cold doorknob. The main features of this exhibit were the woman and a cold doorknob.
- A bible for atheists: a 635-page book filled with blank pages. On the last page it says, "Pending until the second coming." Luderick's mother would like this one.
- A historical account of man surviving a lightning strike, an airplane crash, a rare disease and an electrocution, which, taken together, had a 4.5 billion to one chance of surviving. He died after slipping on a rubber ducky in his bathtub. Dad laughed at that one.
- Failed inventions: hiccup stopper (a variant of the jack-in-the-box); humane fly swatter (a fly swatter with no mesh); and a calendar for optimists—every day is Saturday.

We ate lunch in a restaurant next to the museum that had professional map-folding services. It had this sign: "Will fold maps the proper way! Special—two maps for $2.99." *

This afternoon we visited my paternal grandfather whom I've not seen since I was ten. He lives in a quiet tree-lined retirement trailer park community cloistered behind tall stone

---

* It's common knowledge that once a new map is unfolded, some mechanically inept people have difficulty folding it back the same way unless they use the services of this unique map-folding store. This store employs map-folding experts who have passed a three month university-level course on this specialty. Some of the required courses are:
- Physics of map-folding 206
- Process of map design, production and marketing 101: Trying to fit a long street name with 19 letters in 2mm space
- The Art of Map-folding 312: Japanese paper folding, napkin folding and folding in poker
- Psychological strain experienced by tourists folding a map when driving in an open convertible and steering with their left knee 204

The final exam requires students to properly unfold and fold 24 different sized maps in a compact car without saying the "F" word, knocking over the coffee, or sticking one's elbow into the driver's right nostril. Extra credit is given if the driver does not run over any squirrels.

walls lined with barbed wire on top and has an iron security gate with bars as thick as my forearms. I guess it does a good job of protecting the city from insane and violent senior citizens with walkers. Granddad's mobile home rests on a small manicured lawn beside a short gravel driveway. A classic mobile home with white aluminum sidings, it has a screen veranda surrounding the entrance and a yellow plastic hummingbird with propeller wings on the lawn.

When Mum knocked, an older version of Dad answered, a thin bald man with a white goatee (there's no hope for me—skinniness runs in the family). He cheerfully brought us in and shook my hand vigourously.

"Why, hello Egg! Good to see you again. My, you sure have grown. How's my budding Freudian grandson?"

"Dad, he doesn't want to be a psychiatrist. He aspires to be a Royal Canadian Air Force pilot," my father sternly told him. I beamed.

"That's great Egg!" Granddad said as he patted my back.

After a few minutes of gibberish chitchat, Mum and I went into separate rooms to change into our bathing suits. I changed in Granddad's bedroom. It has a small desk in the corner brimming with papers and scholarly journals and lining the fake wood-panelled walls were rows and rows of textbooks, barely supported by pregnant-bellied shelves. One hiccup would bring the place down. As I gingerly applied sunscreen, I studied the collection of books and could see where Dad acquired his taste in odd sleep-inducing literature:

- *"Greek Accents: a student's manual on how to order pita souvlaki without being punched in the nose"*

- *"Statistical Probabilities of Misspelling the Words 'Yacht' and 'Rhythm.'"*
- *"The Psycho-Social Influence on the Variable Modulations of Linguistic Speech Patterns of Your Voice After Being Kicked in the Nuts."*

While Dad and Granddad were discussing Alfred Adler's theories, Mum and I went swimming in the mobile park pool. No bouncing women in bikinis this time, only sagging 70-year-old ladies in rubber flower bathing caps swimming tediously back and forth. Mum became depressed upon seeing these women.

"They remind me of who I'll become—old and baggy," Mum confided.

"You'll still be my mom," I comforted her.

When we returned to the mobile home, we all went out and played shuffleboard with Granddad's friends. I had the most fantastic encounter with a muscular guy named Mr. Goby. He's an ex-war pilot! During World War II, he flew 22 missions on board the Boeing B-17 flying fortress for the US "Mighty Eighth" Air Force, the 359th Bomb Squadron of the 303rd Bomb group based at Huntingdonshire. The B-17! One of the greatest long-range heavy bombers at the time, it was powered by four immense 1 200 hp Wright-R Cyclone turbocharged radial piston engines that could take it to a ceiling of 35 600 feet at a maximum speed of 287 m.p.h. It was armed to the teeth with 12.7 mm M2 Browning machine guns and could carry a 4 500 lb bomb load for long-range missions. The Norden bombsight made it deadly accurate—it could drop a bomb in a pickle barrel from 10 000 feet. I've a cool poster of it in my bedroom with all the specs.

Mr. Goby told me one harrowing epic daylight battle over Germany. I had a difficult time understanding him, a flamboyant arm-waving man with floppy lips and false teeth that rattled every second sentence. Having never met a former WWII airman before, I raised the volume of my hearing aid to the max and concentrated as if my life depended on it. Given my lifetime familiarity with vintage planes, I was able to match incoherent words with my vocabulary of air force lexicon.

"I was a crack ball-turret gunner, you know, one of those guys who sit underneath the B-17s. One time, a hail of killer anti-aircraft flak hit our squadron of B-17s and there were just chaos—blinding smoke, explosions flashin' and roarin' thunder."

He licked his lips and said, "Out of the smoke, I see a damn Heinkel He 112 fighter zip by and hear this sound of loud popping and strong cold burst of air blew up my butt. I happened to rub my left arm and found it all sticky-wet. Hell, I was shot, my boy, and off the left side was a gaping hole on turret glass—the size of my fist."

He paused to catch his breath and I swallowed my parched throat. He continued, "Once at 34 000 feet, we slam into this rock and roll turbulence. God! I nearly crapped my pants. I thought the plane was gonna rip apart but we high-tailed it back like a dog with its tail between his legs and God bless Tom, he managed to land our baby in a field 50 yards short of the Molesworth army base landing strip. We boys all got out, jumping and hollering and hugging each other like ladies. My arm was streamin' with blood. Didn't feel a thing. You know, the cold froze it numb. We looked around our baby and saw that a big chunk of the vertical tail was shot the hell away. A wimpy He 111 would be eating grass half-hour ago. Not our strong B-17—it had balls of steel. I was taken to the hospital and discharged two weeks later and did 17 more missions. Forty-somethin' years later, I still get bed-wettin', pajama-stickin', throat-dryin' nightmares about that one damn mission. My gawd boy, yer lucky—the worst that could happen to you is fallin' off a bike!"

After this heart-pounding excitement, we said our good-byes and headed back to the hotel to eat and rest. Mum put more cream on my sunburned-fried back. I'm sure my supersonic screams shattered the wine glasses in the hotel bar downstairs

I sent Luderick a postcard with a nude sunbather in front. On the back I wrote, "Lost my virginity 14 times! Too bad you're not here!"

Saturday, February 26: Today was Mum's turn to choose where we would go. This morning, we went to an alligator wrestling show. Due to political correctness and pressure from animal rights activists, they wrestled guys dressed up as alligators and cigarette advertising executives. Dad tried to demand our money back but the woman refused.

When the afternoon rolled around, it was my turn to choose the next activity. Thinking with my primary organ (not the brain), I chose to go back to the beach.

"The sun will make your back even worse," Mum warned me.

Little did she know that my erogenous zones had precedence over the health of my skin. As soon as we settled down on the beach, it became cloudy and windy. Sand blew into our eyes, our towels flipped away and book pages fluttered. We didn't dare dip a toe in the dark forbidding waves. No sweaty women in string bikinis. This disappointment was soothed over by the greatest experience I ever had—a girl kissed me!

When we left the beach to shop nearby, I was allowed go off on my own after promising my folks I would meet them in front of this ice cream place in a hour. I was browsing around a large T-shirt store ("Sale! Three shirts for nine dollars!") when I spied a good-looking Asian girl about my age. She had long, dark hair, large almond eyes and a sweatshirt with "University of Miami" emblazoned across her small chest. After we shyly glanced at each other a few times, she walked over me and cloyingly said, "Looking for something special?"

Imitating James Bond's charm, I winked and replied, "I've been looking for you all my life." She giggled and touched my arm. The touch sent a goose bump thrill through me. I wanted more.

"Where are you from?" she asked.

"Canada," I said proudly, "where we keep each other warm in our igloos under thick fur blankets while watching a hockey game."

She laughed again. "I'm from B.C. and we live in a house," she said with playful firmness. We walked out the store and sat on a bench and talked about everything—our families, interests and life in general. The wonderful part was that she was the easiest person to lip-read. She enunciated each word clearly with no trace of accent, never running them together and with even cadence. Her lips were beautiful and formed the words smoothly. I never understood a stranger so well and this was the longest conversation I've had with a girl without having a nerve-induced coughing fit.

One thing I didn't dare tell her was my disability. My hearing aids were well hidden by my hair and, remembering Mrs. Tautog's lessons, I spoke with my best voice. Why scare her off? I enjoyed myself and time flew by. Before I knew it, it was 20 minutes past the hour I was to meet Mum and Dad.

"Oh jeez, I gotta go, my parents are waiting for me," I said as I stood up.

"Yeah, me too," she sighed, looking at the ground.

Several seconds ticked by in an awkward pause.

What happened next put me in orbit. She took one step towards me, her hands resting on my forearms and, in one natural smooth motion, she kissed me. It was one short kiss, but a real kiss. Her lips felt soft and warm against mine and her hair smelled sweet. My head felt light and airy.

Then she was gone.

I never knew her name.

Mum was pissed off when I showed up, she scolded me for being late and gave the usual speech about worrying about me because we are in another country, I could be kidnapped, blah blah blah. Not one word registered—I was in a love daze. Dad sat on the bench nearby with his crutches by his side.

Pleasure aside, my crispy back itches with maddening intensity. Mum explained the skin across my back is damaged and is drying up and cracking. Even with the cream Mum applies every night, I'm in torment. I guess I'm experiencing the good-times and bad-times suffering all writers have to go through to produce their craft.

The TV news reported that Montreal recorded the highest February temperature in 65 years on this day—plus 15! It was about 17 °C here in Florida today, cooler than yesterday. Dad wasn't happy with this. "We spent a bloody $3 000 to go to a climate only two degrees warmer! I feel I'm like one of those cheap T-shirts covering a college student's car seat," he whined. He was never good with analogies.

Sunday, February 27: Returned from Florida. While we were waiting in the airport, my eyes searched among the sea of faces, hoping to catch a glimpse of the cute Asian girl. I ached see her one more time—I wanted her name, her phone number, her address, anything. When the time came to board the plane, I had to face the awful truth: I'll never see her again.

The flight home was pretty much the same as the flight there, except in reverse and that I didn't want to leave. Through sad eyes, I saw how the lands gradually became whiter and whiter tho further north we went. When we stepped on Canadian soil, the temperatures had plunged to a bitterly cold -13 ºC and a snowstorm howled. Montreal looked the same as it was before we left, as if the warm spell had never happened.

Using another one of his bad analogies, Dad grumbled, "I feel like a small piece of toy a child would shove up his nose."

Monday, February 28: Before heading to the mouse race called school (the working world rat race comes later), I read in the newspaper that yesterday's temperature drop was the greatest ever in 43 years. It went from +15 ºC to -13 ºC in nine hours. I cut out the article before Dad saw it to prevent him from feeling even worse than he already is and using more bad analogies.

Lying in bed in the dark, I thought about the cute Asian girl and re-created the one hour we spent together. I remembered her gentle smile and the way her fingers played with her necklace as she attentively listened to me. Ah, her laugh—she laughed so much at my jokes and it was so easy to tell them. I wish I could transport myself back to that wondrous time. It felt so good. Man, I miss her.

March

Tuesday, March 1st: Mum got a job! She had a job interview a few weeks ago and they called her this morning. It'll be a full-time job at a food production company as a professional coffee taster, starting tomorrow. She's not exactly sure what she'll be doing, but it sounds interesting.

I've always wondered about coffee tasters. Who are they? Are they retired wine tasters? Caffeine addicts? Former chefs? They must follow certain rules about eating hot foods that might burn their tongues and dull their sensitive taste buds. Their version of a sick leave would be "burnt tongue." And what do expert coffee tasters do on their coffee breaks? They might have cigarette breaks. Boy, these folks must be the most alert people in the world—how do they sleep at night with all the caffeine?

On the subject of testers, do they hire people to test new sleeping pills? This is an occupation where you're allowed to sleep on the job. After a day of testing sleeping pills, how can they go home and sleep for the night? They must stay up all night watching bad infomercials for do-it-yourself surgery products. They would be people who wouldn't "wake up" to go to work and drink coffee.

Wednesday, March 2: At the supper table, Mum told us about her first day at work at the food production company.

"All I hafta to do is taste each cup of coffee as they come down dis conveyer belt an' check they're A-OK. I'm not supposed to swallow th' stuff—jest swish it around my mouth and spit it out. If it tastes gawd-awful, I would jest mark the cup's number down on mah clipboard."

Dang! It's 10:18 p.m. and I realized I forgot to go to the Dungeon. Plus, I don't think my sun-crisped back would have been able to take any more punishment. At school, everyone discovered I went to Florida and returned looking like a baboon's butt. They were purposely slapping me on the back all day just to hear me scream. If it weren't for the wondrous Asian girl, I would've formed a negative association between "Florida" and "pain" for the rest of my life.

Friday, March 4: Gym day. It was the first time I had been in the gym since the dance two weeks ago. The gym always has a different feel to it after a dance. I could envision the people, the colourful flashing lights and the sweet-smelling girls I danced with. Sounds of grunting, limbs snapping and Alfonsino's screams in the cold bright gym today was a rude splash of cold water in the face.

I arrived home from school to be greeted by Dad at the door. With a dead serious look on his face, he tersely said, "Your mother wants to see you."

Gulp.

I found her at the kitchen table and the look she gave me was the same as the time she threatened to sell me to a local experimental lab where they test extra-large adult suppositories. She picked up a familiar envelope and shook it at me. The credit card bill! She snooped through my drawers! I felt as if I tumbled off a cliff but was left hanging by the seat of my pants on the ever-present branch you see sticking out in cartoons. If she had scrounged deeper in my sock drawer, she would've found something worse—my pack of nude playing cards from Luderick.

"You have some plainin' to do, young man." When she calls me "young man," it's to absolve her of any responsibility towards any acts of child abuse.

Trying to appear puzzled, I studied the offending paper. It wasn't the bill that was in my drawers (whew)—it was a new credit card bill (argh)! She received it today and new charges were added for the car rental: $2532 plus 18% interest.

"I called th' credit company and dey said th' signature on the receipt for the minimal payment of $20 was 'Egbert Flounder.'"

"Uh...uh...." and I explained the whole story, tried to make it pitiful as possible while the world's smallest violin played in the background. This failed to invoke tears from my mother's plaster-firm face.

"I'll pay this bill but you will 'ave to do all th' dishes, snow shovellin', lawn cuttin' and many other chores for the next six months, starting with tonight's dishes."

This is not bad. I've been doing roughly the same chores in the past five years of my life.

Saturday, March 5: I fell asleep in front of the TV and Mum woke me up at 6:00 a.m. this morning, mouthing into my wobbly eyes, "You didn't do the dishes last night! Go 'n do 'em now!" She wouldn't even let me go back to sleep after doing them. I was so tired.

Not only that, Mrs. Tautog showed her prune of a face in the afternoon and made me talk about my Florida trip while mercilessly correcting my pronunciations. I made sure I didn't say any words with "S" in them.

Monday, March 7: Today, Headmaster Sculpin conducted a surprise locker inspection for what he calls "smut." We all lined up next to our opened lockers as he eyeballed the contents. He fearfully glanced at Jake's locker filled with pictures of dead bodies framed by fake toy grenades and went quickly to my locker. He eyed my exploding and strafing WWII airplane pictures and his lips sneered, "Such violence."

With much anticipation, we watched as Headmaster Sculpin approached and opened Alfonsino's locker, the red-light district of Canterbury. Alfonsino stood by, eyes wide, giving an accurate impression of a hamster dropped in a hockey game. The disciplinarian gaped at his R-rated girlie pictures with what passes for shock and he did this for a little too long. The man needs sex. We all waited with bated breath.

"Such filth, this is disgusting, you..." he exploded and the rest of the words were loud gibberish, hurled at Alfonsino with much spitting and lip flapping, his knobby red finger stabbing his chest. After a few minutes of this, he stopped, pursed his lips as he straightened up, his meaty hands gripping the lapels of his suit. A long silence filled the air as we stood and stared at the frightened little hamster with airplane wing collars.

"Take 'em off!" Mr. Sculpin barked. Alfonsino tore down all the pictures under the headmaster's watchful baggy eyes, each of us cringing with each tear and rip. He was immediately sent home and he was suspended for one whole week.

After the last bell, I walked to my bus stop under darkening clouds and arrived to see a cute girl waiting by the bus shelter. Her hair was done up in a side ponytail under a black brimmed hat and she wore a yellow jacket festooned with safety pins over a pink sweater. Below her red mini-skirt, multi-coloured leg warmers were scrunched around her ankles above her checkered high tops. In short, a fashion opposite of Molly. She caught me staring and gazed at me with her glitter-coloured mascara eyes. Her light pink lips formed the words, "Hi there." She had braces.

"Been waiting long?" I said.

She rolled her eyes and snapped her head, "This is soooo bogus, the bus is way late, I've been here, like," she glanced at one of her five Swatch watches, "Oh my God, hours!" Her hoop earrings swung back and forth as if invisible circus chipmunks were doing a trapeze act.

She babbled a mile a minute about her day at school, saying "As if," "Oh gag me with a spoon," "Way cool," and so on. The word "like" appeared in every utterance. As soon as her playful eyes met mine longer and the conversation became more interesting, it began to rain. She opened her umbrella and continued to babble. Even there was a dry shelter a few steps away, I stood rooted on the spot with high hopes she would invite me under her umbrella. In midst of her telling me about a bra accident, the rain dribbled into my hearing aids and short-circuited them, causing a dreadful buzz that effectively drowned out her perky voice. I dared not to touch my hearing aids or make any scary grimaces. I could only muster every ounce of strength into my lip-reading skills. Right before the bus arrived, she looked at me with a curious expression and muttered something that blew past my lip-reading radar. I bluffed, mumbling something vague in reply. She made an angry face, turned around and ran up the bus steps. I stepped on after her and saw the back of her head bobbing to the rear of the bus. She plopped herself down, crossed her arms and glared out the window. I hesitated with confusion and elected to sit in front away from her. She did look pissed off after all. I sat with my back to her and stared out the rain-streaked window, thinking what to do next while my hearing aids continued to buzz. By the time the bus arrived at the terminus, I peeked towards the back of the bus only to find her long gone. I blew it.

Bad news—Mum lost her job today. Several supplies have been disappearing since yesterday when Mum started work. They unjustly accused her of pilfering them and fired her!

"It's unfair—I wuz picked on cause I wuz new."

With tears welling up her eyes, Mum choked, "Stay in school, Egg. Work hard an' go as far as you can go. I always wished I stayed in school instead of droppin' out and goin' to that damn hairdressing night school. Fat lot it did for me." She blew her nose and plodded to the TV lair downstairs.

The doctor removed Dad's cast this morning. He's happy to get rid of the crutches but was careful to not show his glee around morose Mum.

Tuesday, March 8: A college representative came during Mr. Coley's class and talked to us about post-secondary education. At this point, he stressed, we must have a general idea of what we want to do in the future and if we have little or no clue, we should see the guidance counsellor. No problem-o for me because my plans are already laid out: I will simply go to the Mont Royal Aviation College, learn to fly, join the RCAF to become a career pilot and fly secret war missions here and there. It's imperative we apply soon because the deadline for college applications is at the end of this month.

On the subject of careers, I wondered about gynecologists: How does a man, with utmost seriousness, decide to become a gynecologist? How can a man be able to tell his acquaintances, relatives and grandparents that he aspires to be one with a straight face? When he does become one, how does he honestly explain his job to his children? After a lot of practise, they must become excellent poker players with that good straight face.

What about would-be proctologists? How the hell can they tell people that they want to look in people's arses for a living? They must have a low self-esteem to do this occupation. I think the reason you rarely see a proctologist at dinner parties is because of the very thing they do. Who's going to shake their hands or ask them to pass the chicken? You know, many people have two jobs or two university degrees in something. I wonder if anyone is both a proctologist and a dentist—a job for each hand—one in your arse and the other in your mouth. You must make sure the doctor doesn't switch hands.

If my encounter with the valley girl the other day wasn't enough, I was treated with a confusing sight of Molly arguing with the BMW guy in front of the office building. This tormented me because the first unedited, Freudian ID-driven thought that popped in my mind was, "Does this mean she will come back to me?"

Bored with Latin homework, my mind wandered and I rifled through the stack of papers on the corner of my desk and I came across a piece of blue paper. On the top it read:

Canterbury's Annual Science Fair

Friday, March 18th.

"The science fair!" my head screamed and my ears shushed. Damn! I have nine days to conceive, research and construct a science project as well as to write a ten-page report. I have to roll up my sleeves and focus all my energy into this project and not into other things. Working on the Hurricane Mk IIA model will have to wait. After tomorrow.

Before I went to bed, I found morose and unemployed Mum still sitting in the dim TV room watching, "*Icelandic car rally for the directionally impaired.*" She was in the same place as she was when I left this morning, except that a few empty chip bags were added to the depressing scene.

Wednesday, March 9: I saw Molly on the bus today, sitting alone in the back with arms crossed, her face sullen and distant. I did my best to avoid eye contact but it was difficult to do—her blouse button was undone.

Regarding the science project: my last entry, the glow-in-the-dark hamsters in rocket launchers, didn't go over well with Mr. Barbot and the science department, therefore I cannot make a sequel of the same project. While Mr. Coley talked about "A Brave New World," I struck upon an idea: make a prototype of a close captioned radio for the hearing impaired. Since hearing impaired people like me and anyone who sat within 50 feet from a concert by The Who have difficulty understanding talk radio, I thought it would be good idea if the radio had a lateral scrolling LED screen transcribing the blathering of radio show hosts. The lyrics of songs could be given as well (Bob Dylan's songs and "Louie, Louie" would be good ones to transcribe). If we were able to get the technology of putting words on the TV screen as seen in closed captioning (which I sadly don't have but have seen it), we should be able to do the same with radios.

After school, I went to Radio Shed to find out how I could make my closed captioned radio. I had to explain what "closed captioned" is to the pimply-faced guy with a goatee who was as dim as a movie usher's flashlight. He'd never heard of it, although he did understand the concept of subtitles because his girlfriend has dragged him to foreign movies.

After listening to my explanation, he said, "So, let me get this right—Braille appears at the bottom of the screen for people with bad hearing?"

Despite my efforts, he couldn't help except to suggest I read circuit manuals and talk to a radio station about transmitting the first closed captioned message. At his commission-driven insistence, I bought a large $35 book on electronic circuits. I sat at my desk, plopped the volume under the lamp and began to read. Ten minutes into the book, my eyes crossed and my brain scrunched up—I didn't get past the table of contents. It looked as complex as a trigonometry textbook translated from Japanese into Greek. Dad suggested I talk an old college buddy who is an electronics expert. I nodded gleefully and he called him up. We'll be visiting him tomorrow.

Thursday, March 10: After supper, Dad and I drove to Lachine to see his electronics expert friend, Ted. We drove around in circles on the way there but we found the place. Dad was shocked at the state of his residence. It was an extremely run-down house, the type environmentally conscientious inspectors would avoid if they don't want to waste paper on their report of infractions. Three of the windows were boarded up, shutters were hanging by a screw and the partially bare roof sagged and drooped. The paint was faded and peeling from the rotting wood exterior.

The partially melted snow exposed a lawn infested with weeds, garbage and junk, one being a forgotten lawn mower, handle half-off, abandoned beside an unruly shrub. A rusted wrought iron fence enclosed the so-called lawn that tenuously held back dead weeds from bursting out onto the cracked sidewalk. We pushed open the creaky gate and tiptoed carefully up the warped stairs, avoiding the several dangerous-looking nails poking out. Dad glanced at me and reluctantly knocked on the beaten door. A short, balding man with a blue food-stained cardigan sweater immediately answered the door. I suspected the expiry dates on these foods had long passed.

"Hi there, come in, come in," he said, gesturing us inside. He and Dad exchanged pleasantries and remarked about how long they had not seen each other (six years).

I found Ted to be friendly and effusive while he gave us a tour of his cramped house. Hundreds of radios, televisions and other electronic thingamajigs in various states of functioning were piled in every room. I thought I recognized a radio from an A-36 Apache plane.

"Oh that—my father retrieved it from a crashed plane in a field somewhere in Holland during the 1940s," he explained. Hundreds of small electronic parts littered his countertops, tables and chairs. His office had thousands of electronic books on several bookshelves covering every wall from the floor to the ceiling. Twisted piles of academic papers and computer printouts carpeted the floor of his office, making passage impossible unless you wanted to swim (two phrases readily came to mind: "Publish or perish" and "Sink or swim").

After the grand tour of the post-apocalyptic technological war zone, Ted cleared off his kitchen table and chairs so we could sit and talk about my project. Dad explained my idea of the science project and Ted understood it without questions. He even knew what closed captioning was!

"It's possible have a closed captioned radio," he nodded, "but it's too complicated and expensive to set up for such a small high school project in such a short time." He admits it would've been a historical moment if a radio station were to broadcast the first closed captioned message on the day of the fair, but we have to make do with a prototype.

"Hmmm," he hummed while scratching his white stubble, "I'll tell you what. I suggest we cheat." Dad and I were taken aback.

"Don't be alarmed, all scientists have cheated one way or other. For instance, Newton claimed he discovered gravity when it was there all along."

Ted excitedly explained that we could work together to insert a bar LED screen on a radio that is electronically connected to a keyboard.

"I could listen to the radio through earphones while hiding under a table and type in whatever the announcer is saying. Using special circuits, the people at the science fair will hear a delayed version of the broadcast while I hear the real-time broadcast."

This way, he will have time to transcribe it and make the transcription appear on screen in real-time! Dad spoke up. "This is a smashing idea, but Egg should check with his teacher first to see if he can secure the approval." Ted agreed.

Dad wants me to do most of the work since it's my project and he wants me to learn from it. Ted will teach me how the radio and closed captioning works and let me put a radio together with his guidance. The radio should be shown without its cover to expose its circuitry so people could see how it works. I'll make posters with diagrams and pasted-on explanatory notes to accompany my oral presentation. Having worked out the plan, I promised to talk to Mr. Barbot tomorrow and let Ted know if we can go ahead with it. I hope we can do this because it's either this or go with my idea of genetically engineered square peas that don't roll off your plate.

Friday, March 11: Mr. Barbot accepted the project idea! He said he normally doesn't allow outsiders to be an integral part of a science project but will make an exception for this unique project.

"As long as you don't use fire, explosives, or sharp instruments, the project is acceptable," he warned me. I'll work with Ted this weekend to start the project.

Remembering that Dad's birthday is tomorrow, I went to the shopping centre after school. It's difficult to buy a gift for someone with so few interests. Since he reads odd and obscure books, I bought him a 346-page tome, *"Scattered Hegemonies: Post modernity and transnational feminist practices while holding your family jewels during a free kick in a soccer game."*

I saw Ilisha talking giddily on the phone to a new boyfriend, from the looks of it. Already another one! This bothered me because I'm still single. I can't stop thinking about the missed opportunities with Molly, the Valley girl and the Asian girl I kissed. Every time I see a couple kiss, hug, or even hold hands, I get a yearning achy feeling for someone to love. I've all this "love" energy in me waiting to be released. However, if I meet the right girl for me and let it all out all at once, she will run to the authorities. I would let it out little by little so it would last our lifetimes: sending love notes, playing the boom box under her window, making daisy chains. I wouldn't even pressure her for sex because I'd be satisfied enough with only holding hands and smelling each other.

How the hell can Ilisha get a date with any guy she meets? She's so involved with her volleyball team, student congress and assorted clubs she has no trouble finding time dating guys. My whole social life consists of playing hockey with a paranoid pal and spending my formative sexual peak years at an all-boys school. Being hearing impaired makes it worse—everywhere I go, I'm alone in a sea of perfectly hearing people. Put a duck in a roomful of swans and you'll get one strange lonely duck.

I saw a poor old man shuffling up the street to the grocery store, his back bent over and gripping his cane and this depressed me even more. Will I grow up old and alone? I halfheartedly scanned the personal ad section of the newspaper, thinking in wild off chance there is a girl out there looking for an hearing impaired RCAF-pilot-to-be. No such luck. But, I took liberty with common phrases and supplied my own translations:

"Marriage-minded" = "Before I'm deported"

"Good-looking" = "After a 6-pack"

"Sense of humour" = "I'll laugh at how funny your ears look"

"Intelligent" = "I don't put white-out on my computer screen."

"Athletic" = "See how fast I run away when I meet you."

Being so occupied with the state my poor love life, I forgot to work out again.

Saturday, March 12: Today we celebrated Dad's 50th birthday. He was happy with the book I gave him and he agrees it'll go well with his obscure book collection. Ilisha gave him an after-shave cologne and Mum's present was a pair of new slippers. Mrs. Tautog gave him a small gift before our lip-flapping exercise, a gold bookmark.

For someone receiving four great presents, Dad was morose and depressed all day.

"Don't bother 'im, Egg," Mum whispered to me. "He's not happy about turnin' 50, he's goin' through a midlife crises."

I don't blame him. He suffered through puberty (something I can relate to), the stage where he first grew hair where he never had hair. With hair growing in new areas such as his nose and ears these days, he's entering a new stage: "middle-age puberty." This is the time when 50ish men develop a spare tire, buy Porsches and find all their hair has left their heads to travel out of the ears.

"Hey guys," a single hair speaks up, "the view up here is getting boring, let's all travel to the ear canal!" Before you know it, you'll have little wigs hanging out of your ears like wall plants. If old men let their ear hair grow long enough, they can comb it over their bald heads.

Think about it: my father is way past middle age. The expected life span for men is about 70, so the designation for "middle-aged" should be 35. Being 50 and having only about 20 more years left of his life, I think my father is "three-quarterly-aged."

"Don't tell 'im that, Egg, I don't wanna to hear him moan 'n groan about it anymore than he is," Mum pleaded.

Ilisha talked with her new love for a long time on the phone, laughing and giggling every two minutes. He's a real comedian, one of the few people who can make her laugh this much, aside from me, who can make her laugh only by seeing me naked.

I didn't work out tonight because I needed to start my science project. After his birthday supper, Dad drove me over to Ted's house. Ted spent most of the time teaching me how the radio works while I took notes. So far, so good. I'll be seeing him again on Tuesday.

Remembering my previous business order from Mr. Luderick Bass, I slipped into Ilisha's closet and took the requested item. Dad caught me in the hallway holding my sister's red dress. I froze.

"How kind of you to bring your sister her dress," he said with a hint of pride. Over Dad's shoulder I saw Ilisha's shadow coming up the stairs.

"Yeah, Dad," I quickly whispered. "Don't tell her. I'm gonna get it cleaned." He turned around and blocked Ilisha's way, giving me time to zip into my room before she could see me.

Sunday, March 13: I stayed at Luderick's house all afternoon. I've not seen him since I left for Florida. Out of earshot, his first words were, "Egg! You idiot! Why the hell did you send that postcard? My mother saw the picture of the naked girl and freaked out! She made me say 'Hail Mary' 20 times in Church this morning because she thought I was abusing myself!"

"Well, Luderick, you've been abusing yourself—I know you've been spending suspicious amounts of time behind the locked bathroom door and making funny noises."

"I was reading Parti Québécois separatist literature."

"That explains it—it would make any Anglophone moan."

"Forget it anyway—it was a great pic, Egg. I taped it inside my math book."

Once in his room, I produced Ilisha's dress from my schoolbag and we made the transaction.

"Luderick, I'm curious. We've been making these deals for the past month—what are planning to do with my sister's stuff?"

"Uh, nothing," his face reddened and with a magical sleigh of words, he deftly changed the topic.

"You just make the deals like a real businessman—with no questions asked. Hey—tell me about Florida."

I told him all about my Florida trip, with great emphasis on the girls I saw on the beach (with a few exaggerated details). I didn't tell him about the Asian girl because I prefer to keep that magic moment private.

The St. Patrick's Day dance is next week! I hope Alfonsino has healed enough from his chest surgery to go.

During times of sweaty palms, butterflies in the stomach and nerves strumming like a guitar, his entertainment quells much of our adolescent anxiety around the female species.

Monday, March 14: Alfonsino came back from his weeklong suspension, wearing a sparkly blue ten-gallon hat and faux alligator-skin cowboy boots.

"Hey man, I went to Texas to see my uncle at his farm and, whoo-hee, the milkmaids were like this," he cupped his hands in front of him, as if the girls could only have beach balls under their sweaters.

"They had arthritis in their hands?" I teased him.

"Egg—the hot girls, the sex—it was the best suspension ever," he boasted.

I picked up the application forms for the Mont Royal Aviation College from the guidance counsellor's office after school. As soon as I sat on the bus, I read every word in the application twice. I'm going to fly! I imagined myself, sitting in the cockpit of the sleek Aermacchi MB.339 light attack aircraft, roaring through the sky over majestic mountains, deep clear lakes and blowing away gape-mouthed Jake below.

Ilisha's new boyfriend called during supper. After listening to him for a few minutes, Ilisha burst out in laughter.

"Oh, you want to tell the story to my father?" she asked and handed the phone to Dad. He listened for a few minutes and guffawed (an event as rare as a Progressive Conservative Tax cut). Mum talked to him next and tittered until tears came out of her eyes.

"What was the joke?" I asked my family.

"Oh—you had to be there," Ilisha said.

"It loses its impact with repetition," Dad followed.

"It wuz th' way he said it," Mum's excuse went.

I felt clueless as a bad detective. When will I meet this guy? He seems to be a likable, funny sort.

After supper, I went over to Ted's to work on my project. I managed to finish making the posters and am halfway done with installing a small LED screen on the face of the radio.

I skipped going to the dungeon again. I looked at my body in the mirror and still see the stickman character. Right at this moment, I decided to quit bodybuilding. It was too time-consuming and too much work. I rationalized that having a big muscular body won't do much for me aside from impressing people with my ability to open pickle jars. No matter how much muscle I would've had, I would still be a weak animal in the animal kingdom. We humans often think we're the highest ranking species because of our sophisticated intelligence. However, as physical beings alone and without machines, we are essentially weak and defenseless in comparison to many other animals. Apes are stronger than us. Cheetahs can outrun us. Eagles can spot a fish from a mile up while some of us fumble with eyeglasses.

Since tools and machines are what enable us to be faster and more powerful than any animal, we have become dependent on these same tools and machines. Thus, muscles aren't needed if we have the machines to do the hard work for us. So, why should I bother working out?

Wednesday, March 16: As I waited for my bus, I spotted a strange-looking girl far across the street. She kept glancing at me as I ate my chips. I focused on eating my snack and watched at her from my peripheral vision. Her bus arrived and she waved to me before getting on. I felt a twinge of excitement and, caught off guard, I gave a feeble wave back. Could this mean a new girl in my life?

When I arrived home, I found my parents cleaning the house. Mum was wiping her plate collection and Dad on his knees scrubbing the kitchen floor. Mum put down an Elvis plate, "Grandma Aruana called last night, she'll be arrivin' tomorrow and will stay wit' us for all of next week."

Dad, wearing ridiculous yellow rubber gloves, looked up from a spot on the floor and grumbled, "She sure told us bloody well in advance."

Mum ignored Dad and explained, "Grandma is usually a busy woman, always doin' stuff like doing volunteer work for charities, bein' the president of a senior club in Dallas, an' stuff. It so happens she's free next week to visit us an' she won't get this chance again in a long while."

After supper and cleaning the house, Dad drove me over to Ted's house. I finally finished making the posters and the radio is connected to the keyboard. While I memorized my speech, Ted practised typing out the radio announcer's messages. It's all coming together except for one thing: Ted is a damn slow typist. He types using only one finger. Worse still, he's an awful speller. Since I can never understand what they're saying on the radio, I cannot be sure whether Ted's transcription is accurate or not. He once typed, "De four cats fore two moro is rane and posse billy a bite of snoe." I don't know if he was listening to a Mexican weather forecaster or a cat expert. The science fair is two days away! How can I explain to the audience why the transcript looks so jumbled?

I'm experiencing your-mother-in-law-going-over-the-cliffs-in-your-new-Porsche mixed emotions. The fair is on Friday, the day after tomorrow, and the dance will be the next night. From the perspective of my science project, I want the days to pass by slowly. However, speaking from my libido zones (an uncharted territory near Bimini), I want the days to come fast. Mum says it's like taking off a bandage. There are two ways of doing this: the quick way and the slow way. "No matter which way ya do it, you'll still yank off some hair."

Thursday, March 17: Today is Saint Patrick's Day and half of the school wore green. Mr. O'Porgy wore a green sweater vest with a button that suggestively said, "Kiss me, I'm Irish." I don't think this was appropriate given Canterbury is an all-boys school.

Grandma Aruana arrived at 5:30 p.m. when we were about to eat supper. She looked older than the last time I saw her but she hasn't lost a bounce in her step and her perky personality. She carried two heavy suitcases up the stairs to the guest room while refusing my help (See? I don't need muscles after all).

After supper with Grandma, I went over to Ted's and we worked on the remaining details of my science project. Ted has been practicing his typing and is better, although he still makes spelling mistakes. Despite his slow typing and atrocious spelling, I think it'll be a success tomorrow.

Friday, March 18: 7:03 am. I tossed and turned all night like a trout on the bottom of a boat because my mind was preoccupied with two things: the answer to the question, "What is the name of the thing that hangs down at the back of the mouth?" and the damn science fair. I was so nervous, I had the chills. I feared my mind would go blank, my voice would squeak like a rusted gate, my hands would tremble so much that Mrs. Catfish could use them for making milkshake. Doing oral presentations in public speaking class was never a problem; I'm in front of my own peers and I wing it. At the fair, there will be the whole school population, all the teachers and parents, only a fraction of them know I'm hearing impaired and why I speak like a Scotsman with post-nasal drip.

11:34 pm. The dreaded science fair day finally lumbered by and is receding into the distance. It was an awful day. Today's one redeeming feature was that facing the inevitability of my mortality in gym class was postponed until next week. We had our regular classes in the morning and the fair wiped out the afternoon courses. After lunch, we all went into the gym to meet our parents to set up our projects. I saw Dad, Mum and Grandma right away but Ted wasn't with them.

"Don't worry my boy, Ted will be here shortly," Dad reassured me. I busied myself with setting up the radio and posters. At precisely 1:25 p.m. Headmaster Sculpin stepped up the podium, gave a short introduction and announced the rules:

1) Each student or group of students will be randomly assigned a time slot at which they will present their project.

2) Only ten minutes are allocated for each project (Kyle and his tree sloth tricks were doomed).

3) Any project incurring dismemberments and/or fatalities or will be deduced five points.

4) Each project will be judged according to ingenuity, originality and presentation by three judges: Mr. Fry, Mr. Sauger and Mr. Sculpin.

He read out the order and times of the presentations. When he announced that the lucky first presenter was Alfonsino Troutio, a scream was heard in the back.

"He's not prepared at all," I thought to myself as I saw his forehead straining with intensity before he rushed into the bathroom. This was the most thinking he has ever done since he learned to tie his shoes. Being fourth, I was to present my project at exactly 2:10, ready or not. At 1:30, Headmaster Sculpin, with considerable effort, pulled the trigger of a starter pistol into the air to signal the official commencement of Canterbury's 78th annual science fair.

"Now, I will introduce our first presenter, Alfonsino Troutio." All eyes swivelled to a quivering boy in platform shoes and lavender dinner jacket with wide lapels.

Having decided his project's topic two minutes ago, he aptly chose to give a scientific-sounding explanation of his recent wig-removal surgery. Since posters with pasted on explanations were a required aspect of the project, Alfonsino creatively substituted this by using crude diagrams drawn on toilet paper with his mother's lipstick. During his description of the grafting procedure, a shocked look of disapproval from the faculty rose when he graphically showed where the skin came from (a bit plagiarized from David Scalen's moon model).

Unfortunately for him, there was only so much to talk about. A large proportion of his presentation was spent in silence, punctuated by his asking, "Any questions? Any questions?" every 30 seconds to a stunned but unimpressed audience. Headmaster Sculpin scowled so much I thought he was going to have movement right then and there in the panel chair. I can imagine Alfonsino making up for this by writing a 20 000 word paper on the origins of wool socks without using the letter e.

Carl was the next presenter, he did a harebrained presentation using his cat to test the Steven Wright thesis: If toast always lands butter side down and cats land on their feet, what happens if you strap a piece of toast on back of a cat and dropped it? A stepladder and a petrified cat were the main features of this project. He lost points chasing his cat around the gym each time he tested the scientific hypothesis. I didn't pay much attention because I was preoccupied with the fact that Ted had not arrived yet. When I was watching Carl's attempt to detach the cat from Mr. Sculpin's leg, a horrifying realization hit me—I forgot my notes! Damn! I pictured my whole three-page speech sitting on my desk at home and gave a pained moan. I began trembling like a cold dog, my throat became dry as a funeral march and sweat dripped from my pounding forehead. Sensing my mounting anxiety, my Dad, paid to recognize these things, tried to reassure me again.

"Don't worry, Egg. He'll be here shortly."

My mind raced and my heart pounded in my bony chest. "Shortly?" I thought. Define "shortly," Dad! Upright-walking humans evolved "shortly" after the dinosaurs and that was millions of years! Grandma put her arms around me, a comforting hug.

Jake was next and his presentation was an R-rated explanation of bloodstain patterns in crime scene analysis. He presented graphic photos of maimed people and blood splatters to the horrified parents and faculty. I think I saw myself in the corner picture, my head hanging off the art class table.

While Jake demonstrated various knife wounds with his 12-inch hunting knife, I kept glancing at the entrance, which became crowded with wide-eyed parents slowly backing away. It was 2:07 and my turn was up in a few minutes.

"Ted is not here! Ted is not here!" my frazzled brain echoed as my nervous stomach did flip-flops. I stared at Mr. Sculpin's stopwatch, hoping to send it telepathic signals to slow it down. The watch's split second timing ticked on.

"Time's up!" Headmaster Sculpin sharply bellowed, abruptly cutting off Jake as he was about to demonstrate something with Carl's poor cat.

"And now, Mr. Egbert Flounder will give his presentation."

Grandma Aruna patted me on the shoulder, "Go for it, you can do it."

I walked to my project table and the judges and 80-odd people turned to me. Headmaster Sculpin eyed me intensely and said the dreaded words, "You may now begin." My mind went absolutely blank, as if a gremlin hid my memorized presentation and a small part of my brain scrambled around for the first sentence of my speech. If I could remember those few first words, it would be followed by the recall of next sentence, then the next paragraph and then whole oral presentation would come back to me.

What was the first sentence? I froze and stood transfixed before the large crowd. All eyes were burning me, an ant under a magnifying glass.

Several long seconds passed by.

My stomach gurgled.

My head ached.

My throat dried up.

At that moment, it hit me—I remembered! The word that came to me was: "Uvula" No! I was supposed to be thinking of something of a more immediate concern, like escaping. All that was seen and heard was Headmaster Sculpin's flared nostrils and impatient breathing. The gym door swung open and everyone's head snapped in unison towards to the entrance. It was Ted!

He tossed me my speech papers, made a thumbs-up gesture and ducked under the table in a blur of movement. I breathed a deep sigh of relief, glanced at my papers and began my presentation. Speaking as best as I could, I began by enunciating my explanation of radio transmission and why hearing impaired people cannot understand talk radio. I pointed and waved at my large, well-illustrated posters (lots of pointing means higher grades). When the moment came to stop talking and to show the project, I switched on the radio. It was set at station 932 AM and I could hear the garble of a man talking away but no words came on screen. Everyone stared and strained to see the small rectangular screen. Several agonizing seconds went by and the screen remained blank. Headmaster Sculpin's nostrils flared up again. An unbearable amount of tension filled the room, 90% coming from me.

Finally, text appeared on screen and it was quick, clear and accurate. Ted typed for a good five minutes and I could see that people were impressed. I was overjoyed! I enthused my concluding comments, saying that while closed captioned radio is not here yet, with time and technology, it may come someday for the thousands of hearing impaired people who need it.

I scored 92%! Unfortunately, I came in second. Bill Bream came in first with his project on the "Phantom limb phenomena and the brain." Dad was fascinated with this and spoke at length with Bill. Grandma was impressed. "I didn't realize that deaf people cannot enjoy the radio. What a marvelous idea you had!"

Dance is tomorrow night! I'm glad the fair is over and done with and I can celebrate it with the dance. I wonder if I'm going to finally meet someone tomorrow night. I figured the more dances I go, the greater the chances of me meeting my future wife. I've boogied at 25 dances in my lifetime and I think I'm due to meet someone special soon. I resolve to do more than to dance, I'm determined to meet a girl, talk to her and ask her out without being a blathering dolt.

Saturday, March 19: Woke up this morning with amazement in my eyes. I couldn't believe the dance was tonight! But first, I had to suffer through another lesson from Mrs. Tautog. We worked on my listening skills; I practised lip-reading her with dance music in the background. After she shuffled off, I showered, chose the clothes carefully and groomed in front of my mirror. I put extra gel in my hair to keep it firmly in place so my hearing aids won't be exposed when I boogied. We had a nice, light supper at 5:30. Grandma told us an amusing story about Giovanni Andrea, an Italian canonist in the 1200s whose extraordinary shortness of stature led Pope Boniface VIII to ask him three times to rise, believing he was kneeling.

When Dad and I sat into the car at 7:00, I was given a scare of my young life. The car wouldn't start. He tried and tried to turn the engine on but it wouldn't catch. He cursed obscure British 14-letter words and beat the car with a small defenseless shrub. I sat there, speechless. My mind raced with horrible questions: What should we do now? How am I supposed to go to the dance? What if I missed it and my dream girl hooks up with "three-nipple" Alfonsino?

"You'll have to take a bus, my lad," suggested Dad.

"But Dad, the bus takes an hour and 15 minutes to get there and I won't arrive before the 8:00 p.m. closing time. A taxi is out of the question as it will cost me an arm and leg and an ear to get there."

Dad threw up his arms, "Then you can't go."

We went back inside and I was in near tears. Grandma saw my gloomy face and came to the rescue. She called a cab and paid for the fare. "Your late birthday gift." I was dropped off in front of the gym and grandma stayed in the car.

"Have a good time and we'll pick you up right after the dance, dear," Grandma chuckled as she gave me a friendly punch in the shoulder.

The dance was especially memorable. I arrived to see Alfonsino in the boy's bathroom using up a whole can of hairspray to stiffen his diving-board pompadour.

"Hey, Egg, dem chicks love a good head of hair."

"Yeah, almost enough to distract them from your ugly mug," teased Bill Bream.

"Watch me, guys," he said as he strutted out.

I followed him to the dance floor and watched him do this weird dance move in front of a gaggle of giggling 9th graders. He came too close to a disco light and his pompadour caught on fire. In the darkness, we saw Alfonsino's head, aglow from the flames, bob and weave through the dark dance floor, followed by what sounded like screams. After a frantic search, he found what he was looking for—the food table. No, he wasn't hungry. Specifically, he was looking for a punch bowl. He doused the flames by sticking his head in the bowl (at least the punch was non-alcoholic). He screamed for the second time when he felt what little remained of his precious hair. His head charred and smoking, he resembled a failed barbecue experiment. He stayed on the dance floor, going by his usual logic, "Since it's pretty dark in there, dem chicks won't notice the missing hair." Yeah, and no one noticed Halley's comet screaming through here.

So, another wonderful night. Unlike the other dances, I met A GIRL! Yes! My lifelong quest is about over. Her name is Demoiselle. The story of how we met will have wait until tomorrow, I'm happily exhausted and need my dreamy sleep.

Sunday, March 20: I opened my eyes to morning sunlight streaming into my room and felt waves of warmth and bliss from the memories of last night's romantic experience with Demoiselle. Dear journal, my life has never felt so good. From the comfort of my bed, I blissfully remembered what happened. After the Alfonsino incident, the lights dimmed and slow music began to float in the air. Reacting to evolutionary instincts of a teenage boy, I began my search for a partner. I was scanning the row of available girls when my eyes locked on another pair of eyes in the crowd. It was she. My heart began to pound.

She was beautiful. The dim lights highlighted her smooth skin and her long brown hair cascading down her willowy body. Her soft brown eyes behind her round glasses met mine, shook hands and said, "Hello."

She began weaving through the crowd towards me. The slow beat of the love song floating through the misty air, our eyes watching each other. She stopped in front of me and said the exact words I'd hoped to hear: "You dropped your mints, here they are."

"Oh, yes—thank you," I sheepishly shoved the package in my pockets.

"Do you want to dance?" she asked. My heart never soared so high since I was on that plane to Florida at 37 000 feet. I gulped hard and nodded a yes. She gently took my hand (wow!) and led me to the centre of the dance floor. We held each other tight and slowly danced. I remember staring at the mirrored ball's projection of thousands dancing stars upon the high walls and feeling her warm body against mine. I blissfully closed my eyes and floated in heaven.

After the ballad died away and the fast music burst from the amplifiers, I asked her to dance again. Even when the fast song ended, we continued to dance. We danced for the rest of the night and took a few breathers, sitting awkwardly side-by-side, our shoulders touching. Conversation was a tongue-tied struggle but our bodies and eyes made up for the lack of words. We sat together, watching the scene before us: the flashing coloured lights, the dancers and the half-baked Alfonsino trying to convince someone to dance with him.

When the final slow song strummed in the air, we wrapped ourselves in each other's arms, embracing our last moments together with eyes blissfully closed. I didn't want this to end.

As the singer's last words faded away, the harsh lights blazed on and reality intruded the dream between two dancers. It signaled the end of what was the most wonderful evening in my life. She gently pulled her soft warm body away from me and with her deep smiling brown eyes locked into mine, she pressed a piece of paper in my hand and disappeared in the crowd. I stood there, my eyes blinking in the bright gym lights and my hand clutching the paper, amazed and transfixed at the turn of events. I shoved the note in my pocket without looking at it. I went outside to meet Grandma and saw that she managed to get the same cab driver to take me home.

As the cab hummed along the dark highway, I gazed out the window at the twinkling city passing by and played the memorable scenes in my mind all the while feeling the paper in my pocket: the girl asking me to dance, the smell of her perfume, her warm body.

Grandma turned around from the front seat and saw the beatific smile on my face. She gave me a knowing look and tapped my knee. "You had a wonderful time, eh?"

I didn't have to answer. I turned towards the silent buildings drifting by, the lights of the city reflecting off the cab windows, wanting to remain in my silent reverie. Grandma didn't blab anything to my parents back home. "I'll keep your secret so you can tell them yourself," she said after she paid the cab driver.

I floated up the stairs and brushed my teeth. Once alone in my room, I closed the door, sat on my bed and took the piece of paper out of my pocket. With mounting anticipation, I carefully unfolded it. It read:

Thanks for the dance, handsome. Call me 555-8372. I want to see you again.

Love, Demoiselle

I stared at the note for a long time, especially at the word "Love." She thinks I'm handsome! Not only that, she wants to see me again! This was the first time I learned of her name. Demoiselle. I repeated it silently. Demoiselle. Demoiselle. Demoiselle. I smelled the note and I detected a faint smell of her sweet perfume. I couldn't believe that she personally gave ME a note! Me! A guy who wears what looks like navigation devices in each ear. I think I'm in love. I'm feel like a new person, excited and scared at the same time; my palms are sweaty, my mind is flighty and my stomach is fluttering.

I spent the whole day reading and relaxing. The feeling is so good I want to savour it, like warm water coating my cold back. Homework was done in the haze of long daydreams of last night. This new wonderful feeling is mine, mine only. A few times I went to my closet to smell the shirt I wore last night, which bore the airy feminine smell of Her perfume.

Mum snapped my reverie while I was eating late afternoon snack. "Mop th' kitchen floor before supper, Egbert,

I've not forgotten th' credit card bill." Damn.

Monday, March 21: It was strange being in school today. First, the dreamy night on Saturday, the suspension of reality on Sunday and hard, cold reality of math equations, rusty lockers and Sculpin's glares today.

I couldn't concentrate all day, my mind kept wandering to far-away lands, filled with visions of Demoiselle's smiling face and soft eyes. But, I have so many questions: What is my next step? Should I call her? How can I talk to her on the phone if I won't understand her? How would she react if she finds out that I'm hearing impaired? Having a big brother would be great help. He would simply slick his hair back, pick up the phone, pretend he is I, and ask her out with a confident manly voice. Why do I have to learn and do everything myself? Ilisha wouldn't help. She would tell her about the time she took me to the hospital after an airplane modelling accident that resulted in my finger being glued up my right nostril.

Guess who I saw after school? Molly! As she walked alone in the opposite direction on St. Jacques Street, she smiled at me and said "Hi" as she strutted by in her high heels. I felt the familiar tingle rush up my spine and smiled back. I said in my mind, "Nope, not this time. I'm taken." But oh man—she looked hot.

Rounding the corner, I saw the strange-looking girl across the street again. She was waiting for her bus, glancing at me and giving meek little waves with her white-gloved hands as I walked by. This time I had a good look at her and shuddered. Ugh, is she ever ugly! That dress under the puffy winter coat—where did I see it before? She embarked on her bus before I was able to figure this out.

I complained about my lack of a big brother at the supper table and it became uncomfortably quiet. Dad, Mum and Grandma looked at each other in a suspicious way. I think Ilisha noticed. For a moment, Grandma looked at me as if she was about to tell me something important but Dad interrupted her and began to tell us about a difficult group therapy session he had with seven patients who each argued that they were Jesus and the others were frauds.

Tuesday, March 22: We had public speaking class this morning and as usual, I didn't know my presentation was due today. I had a brainstorm and managed to scribble a few lines about time travel during Jake's speech about serial killers in the Hollywood area.

According to scientists, especially those who tend to make quotation marks in the air with their fingers, travelling into the past or future is theoretically possible. The practicality of doing this in reality is what makes it impossible, but all agree time travel is ideal especially if you owe Revenue Canada. Imagine time as a long flat ribbon where time progress from point A to point B in a linear manner, except for boring Latin classes. If we were able to fold this ribbon such that point A touches point B, you'll be able to travel the same distance in the next second.

Someone made an interesting analogy of going from one apartment to another that share the same wall but are in different buildings. The only physical way one can travel to the next apartment is by going down the elevator, walking outside to the building next door, bypassing James the doorman and going up the next building's elevator. If time were compressed or folded like a ribbon, a person would go through the wall to enter the next apartment. The concierge would freak out when he sees the hole in the wall.

As for travelling into the past, the distinct problem is replicating the events exactly as they once occurred. At any given moment, all the molecules and atoms occupy a very unique configuration in the entire space out there, from the rock on a planet billions of light years away to the dirt under your nails. Atoms are always on the move. If one goes into the past, can the entire group of atoms be made go back to occupy the exact same configuration? Can all chemical and physical reactions reverse: water becoming oxygen and hydrogen, rust turning into shiny steel, fire un-burning logs, food recombining in the intestine to become whole and pop out the mouth?

What about human and plant life? Equivalent to rewinding a movie on human life, can all people in the world shrink back to the pre-born state and the dead reverse decay and become human bodies once more only to shrink and slide back in their mother's wombs, blastocysts combining instead of dividing, DNAs unraveling, sperm swimming backwards, again and again for each previous generation until the time traveller reaches the past time destination? This would be practically impossible.

Travelling into the past is also a philosophical conundrum because when you arrive, say, the year 1807, the present time year 1983, becomes your future. Yet, when you are in 1807, the year 1983 also becomes your past since you left it only a few minutes ago, leaving your dry cleaner wondering where you went. Question: if you wanted to go back to 1983, do you travel in the past or into the future?

Mr. Bonito found this to be a good speech except it had little to do with the entertainment industry, this month's topic. He gave me 72% for my efforts. Alfonsino, half of his hair still gone from the fire incident at the dance, talked about different acting techniques which included a three-minute imitation of what a bad actor does when he overdramatizes the pain of a pinprick.

Bill Bream later told me what Mr. Bonito bellowed at Alfonsino: "This is an oral presentation, Mr. Troutio, not drama class for the mechanically inept. Your grade is 51%."

I saw the ugly girl again while shovelling the snow off the walkway at home. After two minutes of giving me little waves, she crossed the street towards me, walking as if her legs descended from a tall moose. She stopped 20 paces away and shouted, "Hi, my name is Edith, what's yours?" in a high pitch voice, her heavy makeup cracking around her cheeks. She had so much makeup that if you lit a match, her face would blow up.

"Egbert," I shouted back and rested the shovel under my chin. A few moments of silence passed by as she stood there, not knowing what to say next.

She glanced at her watch and squeaked, "Oh gosh darn, my bus is coming! Bye!"

She lumbered down the street, a giraffe on high heels, her legs moving here and there as if they've never been introduced. The bus stop was in the opposite direction.

This was a strange encounter. Oddly, she looked somewhat familiar. Scrape off all the makeup, I'm sure I would recognize her.

Ilisha talked to Donny again on the phone while we were eating supper. Mum, Dad and Grandma listened in and laughed. I tried to look as depressed as I could, making "I'm feeling left out" faces, but Mum scolded me, "Egg, stop that moaning noise, we can't hear Donny."

Grrrr.

Thursday, March 24: After much internal debate, I've decided to not call Demoiselle because she'll find out about my hearing impairment. Since I've been waiting many years for a girl to come into my life, I have to play it safe. I'll try to get her address and write to her.

I saw the ugly girl in the park near my home, doing the same idiotic waves and grinning like a possum eating persimmons. First, I see her near the bus stop at school, while shovelling and today at the park. Why is she following me like a bad smell? Determined to find her identity, I sprinted up to her. When I was within 30 feet from her, her eyes widened and she picked up her knobby knees and bolted. I gave a short chase and lost. I've never seen a girl run so fast in high heels in snow before. Her style of running was so ungainly: feet pointing east and west, knees bouncing high, elbows sticking out like open car doors.

I stepped into my home bent over, breathing hard. In the living room, Mum was with a gaggle of ladies and, in a loud and clear voice in front of them, announced, "Egbert, I got rid of your old underwear 'n I bought ya new ones. They're on yer bed." The ladies tittered.

There must be mothering rule they teach in parent effectiveness training class that states you must embarrass your children in front of company. Finding second wind, I bounded up the stairs into my room. After composing myself, I looked in my underwear drawer. Mum threw out most of my old underwear! Even my favourite backup ones!

I know this is supposed to be a man's secret but I will tell you that in every guy's dresser, you'll see backup underwear which are the old, transparent, Swiss cheese pieces of cloth we keep in case we run out of the good ones. Since we have backup goalies in hockey, second-string quarterbacks in football and pinch-hitters in baseball, why not extend the male's domain to underwear? Same as keeping old car parts, broken tools and all kinds of nuts and bolts, we guys live in a misguided belief that they will be useful someday. With time, we men can develop a sentimental attachment to these underwears in the same way women have towards their wedding dress. This tells you the strength of our sentimentality.

My new underwear are the pastel-coloured bikini type and two sizes too small. I might as well be prepared to join the RCAF—they wouldn't have sneak saltpeter in my mashed potatoes.

Friday, March 25: I went to the post office after school and traced Demoiselle's address and postal code from her phone number. She lives three blocks from my school!

Ilisha invited Donny over for supper and he arrived in his Land Rover after playing an AA hockey game for the St. Coregon Cougars (and scored two goals). Much excitement and hubbub reigned over meeting him. He's a tall curly-haired guy with thick hands and barn-door shoulders. He has a voice that boomed as loud as a slap shot off the boards; it jangled the dining room chandelier and my nerves. The cat hid under the sofa until he left. He was a relentless producer of witty repartees, boisterous stories and hilarious one-liners that kept everyone, even me, in stitches. My stitches, however, was a product of an over-consumption of spaghetti. I didn't understand a single funny line!

"What was the joke?" I would ask.

"Oh—you had to be there," Ilisha said, waving me off.

"It loses its impact with repetition," Dad explicated.

"It was th' way he said it," Mum's excuse went.

Grandma would say nothing.

Donny would repeat it for me, but I would still not understand him. Rather to have him repeat for the fifth time, I would give an accurate Academy award-winning performance in fake laughing.

Contrary to what most people believe, speaking loud doesn't help hearing impaired people like me understand. Their mouths become wobblier and the words come out like an amplified distorted mush. It's comparable to turning up a Pavarotti tape—his words will still come out Italian.

Giving up on any chance of understanding, I sat silently through supper with my head down, absorbed in my food and wished that my entire family was struck with immediate hearing impairment. Let's see how they would feel! I was the first to finish dessert and when I was about to go into my room, Grandma stopped me in the hall and handed me her napkin.

"No thanks, Grandma, I already wiped my mouth."

"No, no," she said. "I wrote all his jokes down. It's on this napkin." I stared at it incredulously. "I figured you missed everything. You didn't fool me with your fake laughing!"

I sat down at my desk and read the napkin. Yes, his jokes were good and I even laughed at a few. He made a joke about a guy who covered his eyes when he sneezed to prevent them from popping out. I wish Grandma could do this for me every time we have supper.

I wrote a nice, interesting letter to Demoiselle about how wonderful I felt about her and our time together. I ended it by telling her how much I like her and that I hope she writes back soon.

Saturday, March 26: I woke up at 9:00, a feat for me on a Saturday morning, to mail Demoiselle's letter before the 9:30

a.m. pick up. After breakfast, it was time for Grandma to fly back to Texas.

Before hugging her goodbye, she faced me and sternly said, "Only you can make deafness a handicap and don't you do it. You're as good as the rest of them."

She ducked into Dad's car to be driven to the airport. I hope I'll see her again soon.

Mrs. Tautog agreed with Grandma's comment. "It's true, you can be as good as a hearing person if only you think that way."

Sunday, March 27: I went over to Luderick's place this afternoon and when his door opened, I was greeted by a sight that has been haunting me for the past several weeks: the ugly girl!

"Uh, is Luderick here?" I asked.

She stood there with the door open, fluttered her gaudy fake eyelashes and smiled. She was letting cold air in. I stared at her familiar face. OH MY GOD! So, that's why Luderick has been buying Ilisha's clothes!

"Luderick!" I yelled incredulously. "Halloween is seven months away—what the hell are you doing dressed up like my sister?"

With no sense of shame or embarrassment, he replied, "It just feels good." Thankfully, his mother left last week to visit her brother in Edmonton. She would've popped a few vessels seeing him in a drag.

While he wiped off his makeup (I was trying to keep a straight face and a mind as open as the plains of Saskatchewan), he told me how he discovered a new conspiracy. Luderick noticed that CBC TV was presenting American shows.

"Why would a Canadian TV station present American programs to us Canadians? You know what? CBC is really owned by an American corporation and they plan to take over Canada! They're brainwashing us! Soon we'll be buying five guns for every man, woman and child, talking in funny twangs and eating processed American cheese!"

I calmed him down and assured him that Canada is not about to become America's 51st state.

"Luderick, Canada has been resistant to every external effort to become American." I recounted the big U.S. military fiasco of 1972 in Alberta to prove my point. In the summer of 1972, a group of disgruntled American soldiers defected from the army (at this point, I had to explain to him that "defected" had nothing to do with bowel movements). They banded together to form a small renegade group of revolutionaries called, "A Small Renegade Group of Revolutionaries." They thought they struck fear in man by virtue of the fact that cockroaches always ran away whenever they turned on the kitchen light.

Their objective, aside from saluting to every American flag, was to invade Canada and make it part of USA. They thought Canada was nothing but a large prairie populated by 314 bilingual Eskimos and lumberjacks who subsists on beer and maple syrup and live with moose and polar bears. Their plan was to simply walk into Canada and capture the country while we were watching a hockey game. Once done, they were going to declare Canada to be their 51st state to be named later.

Their plan was partially successful. They managed to get by the border guards by lying about their possession of cigarettes, alcohol and weapons. And this was in spite of the fact they were driving a Sherman tank. Anticipating below freezing temperatures and trying to pass for a resident Canadian, they wore large Canada goose down parkas, thick toques and rabbit fur mitts.

Upon their arrival to the first town in Alberta, they were agog—Canada had electricity, running water and no snow. Above all, it was warm. It was July and the hockey season was far over. Realizing their mistake, they did a NFL football-style huddle and came up with a plan B: fight and conquer. They charged up and down the streets, looking for able-bodied men to attack but soon passed out from the heat and were taken to the hospital.

After they recovered, the Americans were surprised by the Canadians' politeness and kindness. They could scarcely believe their ears when they heard words such as "Please," "Thank you," and "You're welcome." They noticed if you stepped on a Canadian's toe, *they* would be the ones to say "Sorry." The members of "A Small Renegade Group of Revolutionaries" felt guilty about trying to invade such a nice country and confessed their attempted takeover. As a punishment, they were forced to pay duty taxes on their smuggled goods and write, "I must not invade Canada" 500 times. They were sent home and the incident was treated the same way as any other embarrassing international incident, covered up and classified as, "Top secret: do not even tell your pet gerbil." Since then, U.S. has never tried taking over Canada again and will never do so.

This story appeased Luderick somewhat, although it had little to do with U.S. content on Canadian TV.

"Ok, I guess we're safe. I'm calm now," he sighed. We didn't make any more business transactions with Ilisha's garments.

"No, Egg. I can't afford them anymore." This meant I had to sneak back Ilisha's earrings and necklace.

Monday, March 28: This morning at school, we walked in French class and found a gorgeous blond babe in a tight white blouse and short black skirt standing before the blackboard, the breed of women you would see in a porn mag, but with clothes on.

Alfonsino, with a grin that betrayed his smutty thoughts, adjusted the crotch of his pants, slicked back his remaining hair and walked up to her as if he was in a singles' bar. He whispered something in her ear.

"Monsieur, can you translate that into French for the class?"

Thinking hard (you could see his head bulging), he stammers, "Uh, Je.. je...veux...coucher....uh...," he turned to her and asked, "Uh, what's hotel in French?"

"Asseyez-vous, Monsieur." He slapped into his seat, an eager dog waiting for his treat.

It turns out that Mr. Poisson is sick and the babe is his daughter Julie. She will substitute for him for the next few days. Today, I never saw our class so attentive, so well behaved and Alfonsino take such great interest in French. Normally the only things French he's interested in are French kissing, French ticklers and the morning-after French toast.

At supper, Mum ate little, her eyes darting around the table. She spoke up, "I've an important interview tomorrow with th' boss of a large company who's very mean."

Someone at the employment office told Mum that this man eats junior executives for breakfast and has a hobby of collecting different ways of firing people. At a 10th anniversary party given to the company's hard-working assemblers, he brought out a large birthday cake with the words, "Happy Layoff." He has used the services of a singing telegram to warble, *"Take this job and shove it."* to the soon-to-be unemployed. His best method of all was using boats to spell out "You're fired" while the hapless executive flew overhead in the boss' private jet. Mum wants the job as the company's secretary desperately even if it means working for this sadist.

Tuesday, March 29: In the locker room before class, I caught Alfonsino spraying something on his neck that smelled similar to a farm.

"It's an illegal sexual attractant, Egg," he said in hushed tones. "I ordered it from Sweden. It's made from bull's testicles and Miss Julie Poisson will go wild. You'll see!" He patted me on the back as I eyed the pictures of naked women pasted inside his locker. He had put up new pictures. I sighed at the realisation that he had not learned anything from his suspension.

In French class, Alfonsino was last to enter and ambled with deliberate slowness past Miss Poisson. She sniffed the air with a puzzled expression. She sat up, straightened her short skirt and said, "Bonjour classe."

"Bonjour Madame Julie," sighed the class.

She sniffed the air again and said, "Je sens une odeur de vache. Qui sent la vache dans la classe?"

All hands shot up. Yes, we smell a cow. While Miss Poisson taught us the vocabulary of different animals, Alfonsino tried to rub the cow smell off with little success. For the whole day, he smelled like a pasture. His neck and face became, ever so slightly, faint at first and darkening by the end of the day, a light shade of green.

"What's this crap!" Alfonsino angrily shook the cologne bottle as we put on our coats to head home. He stared at the bottle incomprehensibly, threw it in the garbage and stomped out. Bjorn, an exchange student from Sweden, gingerly picked out the bottle, read the label and laughed.

"Hey guys, this is not a cologne! It's a potent chemical additive to make grass greener—it's a manure imitation." He read and translated the directions, "Look how strong it is, it says here, 'add one drop for every ten litres of water to nourish one acre of lawn. Wear heavy rubber gloves during handling.'"

On the bus, I saw Molly sitting in the back, talking to another older guy from university. She didn't notice me at all and while the guy blabbed away, she flipped her hair, coyly eyed at him up and down and licked her lips seductively. The guy didn't even notice! If I was in his place, I would've seductively eyed her back.

Back home, Mum was in a great mood and at the supper table, she asked us, "Guess what?"

"They published the sequel to the book, '*The Baking Powder Controversy*?" Dad answered.

"No!"

"You invented the solar-powered toothbrush!" I joked.

"No! I got the job!"

So, Mum will work as a secretary for the cruel boss at a company called, "Monopoly Conglomerate Corporation Company, Inc." She starts tomorrow. Mum says the job pays well and hopes she can keep it for a long time. She wants to save up enough money to buy a giant satellite TV so she can get "*America's Soap Opera Awards for Supporting Plant Roles.*"

Wednesday, March 30: Alfonsino came to school with a large bandage on his neck and smelled heavily of a mixture of cow and medicinal cream. Examining the edges of bandage, I could see that his neck had become a bright shade of green. Not only that, he was itchy; he often scratched furiously through his bandages. He didn't bother to show up for French class and avoided Miss Poisson in the hallways, even if it meant ducking into the janitor's closet. Many students made fun of him, bellowing, "Moooo" as they passed him by.

Demoiselle should receive my letter any day soon. I hope she doesn't think I'm a few spoons short of a place setting and not write back to me. What's the reasonable length of time to expect a reply before I can write another letter?

What if she does write back with a favourable letter? What should I do? How would I progress the relationship? I wish I had an older brother to tell me what to do, with step-by-step, paint-by-numbers instructions. He would tell me everything including how to kiss someone who also wears eyeglasses without having them clink together. I complained to Mum and Dad at the supper table about the pain of being the only son. They looked at each other and didn't say anything. Ilisha and I glanced at each other. The air was pregnant with uncomfortable silence.

Dad spoke up, "Dora, how did your new job go?"

"Oh yes!" Mum exploded and Uncomfortable Silence was born. For the rest of the dinner hour, she told us about her new job and how everyone avoids the boss as if his body odour is potent enough to affect the earth's electromagnetic fields.

Thursday, March 31: I made a shocking discovery when I was cleaning out my desk last night. Under the pile of failed math quizzes, I discovered my Mont Royal Aviation college application. Fudge! I forgot all about it!

"Argh!" I grunted in an Incredible-Hulk-in-the-can voice when I found out that the deadline is April 1st—tomorrow! I stayed up until 2:30 in the morning bleary-eyed filling out the forms and answering all sorts of questions, including the ones about my vaccination records. Not only that, I had to write a three-page essay on why I'm seeking a career in aviation. I had to wake up my parents to have them fill out the financial support forms and answer a few questions. They could barely contain their pride in me applying for college and made little happy grunting noises as they squinted at the application and scribbled in the dim light.

"This beats the time you woke us up to make your porcupine costume for your elementary school play on the very day of the play," Dad reminisced groggily.

On my way out this morning to mail the college application, Mum stopped me, "Are you only applyin' to one school—what if they don't accept ya?"

"This is the only school I want to go to, Mum," I replied. Jeez, she knows how to pop my balloon.

I had hoped to see my fellow students lining up in the Canada Post office mailing in their applications but I was the only student there. I mailed the package by express post so it'll arrive tomorrow.

Molly was on the bus again today with the same university guy she was with yesterday. While he was talking, she undid the top button of her blouse while giving him a sultry look. Unbelievably, the guy didn't react! He was glancing at another guy from the same university. Again, she didn't see me but at least I grabbed an eyeful of her bra.

We had a few relatives over for supper. My uncles Benton, Leo, Nigel and aunts Thelma and Pauline were there along with my cousin Reg. Uncle Leo, a greasy shoe salesman with a fetish for women's feet and a red-nosed alcoholic, is the only unmarried uncle I have.

Mum talked a mile a minute about her new job at the mega corporation for the most part of the dinner over Uncle Leo's nonsensical slurring. While we were slowly eating dessert and listening to aunt Pauline's story about her appendectomy, the phone rang. Leo grabbed the phone from behind him and answered it.

"Il li li hello… no, there's no one here named Egg…What? ….Go away!" He burped and hung up. I sat still in my chair, a spoonful of tapioca pudding hanging in mid-air—it was for me! Who was it?

Everyone stared at Leo and me, their eyes bouncing between the two of us.

Mum burst out, "Leo! Dat call was for Egbert! People calls him Egg."

"Oops," Leo slurred. "I didn't know. It was some chick, named Demo-something, she might call back." He took another swig of wine. A bolt of shock went through me and I felt as if I was punched in the stomach. It was Demoiselle! She called!

"Egg, were you expectin' a call from a girl?" Mum asked, her eyes intense.

My face went hot. "Uh, no maybe it was the wrong number."

"Anyway, when they stitched me up," Pauline continued her story. "They used staples this big…" Everyone went back eating dessert and the mysterious call was forgotten.

I felt a triple mixed reaction—part excitement (because she called me), part puzzlement, (how did she get my phone number?) and part agony (drunken Leo hung up on her). Visions of Demoiselle dumping me and me as a 73-year-old virgin merged in one horrifying image. I lost my girl before I had a chance to kiss her! Years of pining and working for a girlfriend went down the drain along with a few greasy strings of hair and a swill of vodka.

April

Friday, April 1st: We had no school today because it's Good Friday. Mr. Fry must be glad that Good Friday happened to fall on April Fool's day this year, as he would've been Jake's ultimate victim. Jake would've loved to use his assortment of miniature bombs, shock prods and spring-loaded chocolate candy.

Despite the holiday, I'm lacking appetite, lethargic, mentally inert and have taken abnormal interest in the parliamentary proceedings on TV. In short, I'm depressed. Yesterday's events convinced me that all hope is lost.

Donny was here to pick Ilisha up for her volleyball game an hour ago. He punched me in the shoulder when I shuffled by.

"Hey, Egg!" he boomed and my remaining cochlear hair cells were blown back. "How's it goin'?"

"Fine," I said feebly. I rubbed my shoulders and ducked into the kitchen to make my peanut butter and banana sandwich, my only meal of the day. He has no respect for the emotionally dead. Dad came out of his den, something he wouldn't do unless the house was on fire, and talked briefly with Donny in the living room. I had no clue what they said, but from the tone of their voices, they were exchanging pleasantries. Score one for Ilisha, Dad fancies this one.

Saturday, April 2: My depression weighs me down but things are looking up. While I was mulling over Thursday night's surprise call, it dawned on me: I know how she found my phone number! She did the same as I did, but in reverse—she used the address in my letter to get my phone number! This realization perked me up. She did that for ME!

Another thing that perked me up was when I was in the kitchen. I was blithely making my PBB sandwich and looked out the window and caught a sight that made my eyeballs pop out of their sockets. In the living room of the house behind ours, I saw our neighbour's 20-year-old daughter topless. Yes! Topless! I watched her walking back and forth in front of the large window talking on the phone until Mum walked in the kitchen and caught me leering. She shot me one of those patented glares that would've made Hannibal and his elephants turn back. I yanked my eyeballs back into my eye sockets and red faced, resumed making my sandwich. An hour passed and fishy-lips Mrs. Tautog rang the doorbell for our weekly speech lessons. Looking at a wrinkled prune of a face and yellow teeth made my Johnson retract like a frightened turtle after a brief stretch in the sun.

At the supper table, Mum announced we all are going to church for Easter Sunday tomorrow. She glowered directly at me when she said this.

Sunday, April 3: True to her word, Mum woke us up early this morning to go to church for Easter. I hate going to church because I never could understand the priest's mumbles and it's boring after the first five minutes. This priest talks with absolute minimal lip movement and he speaks so low that half of the congregation is on the wrong page of the bible. He could be reading his grocery list and no one would notice. What also annoys me is that we stand up and sit down too many times, a ploy, I'm sure, to locate those who are sleeping.

On our way in, I saw a notice on the bulletin board that read, "The evening service on Wednesday, April 6th will feature the sermon topic of 'What is Hell?' Come early and listen to our choir practise." Dad laughed at that one. As usual, my family parked our butts near the front, so I "would understand the priest better." I could stand nose-to-nose to him and still would not understand him. Regardless, he's a nice guy and all, is friendly and says "Good day" to everyone he meets, including mannequins and headrests of parked cars.

After we sat down, I saw a neatly dressed and combed Luderick and his mother, stern and stock-still, sitting in the pew behind us. The dreadful woman leaned over to me and pontificated, "Egbert! Glory is *Jesus*, your body and holy soul is finally under the eye of *God* in this great temple of his loving heart. Pray and may the great *Lord* grant you the miracle of hearing…" and so on. I nodded along, trying to appease this fearful woman. Luderick sat behind her, trying to suppress his laughter.

Over the incomprehensible murmuring emanating from the priest, I stared at the gruesome R-rated statue of Jesus nailed to the cross hanging behind him. Wouldn't the crucifixion have been more humane if they used Velcro? After an excruciating three hours, I start to fantasize that the statue falls off its moorings and crushes the droning priest. It never happens.

My mind wandering from my usual fantasies of Molly, Demoiselle and flying a F-86 Sabre (occasionally involving all three), I thought about something interesting: Don't you think that the Catholic God sounds suspiciously like Santa Claus? Think of the omnipotent, omnipresent and immortal God and Santa fits the bill: he has a white beard; he has several elves helping him; he watches us all the time; he has a list of those naughty and nice; he is immortal and has no backstory.

We can agree that Santa Claus is a mythological figure designed to make children behave ("If you throw squash at your brother, you won't get any presents"), but isn't this what the idea of God does too? If you so much as to steal a chocolate bar because you are too poor and hungry, you'll go to hell. They say that if you pray to God, he will listen and this is the same idea as sitting on Santa's lap and telling him what you want for Christmas.

A few more burning questions. First, the classic question: Can God create a weight so heavy that he cannot lift it? If he is both immortal and omnipotent, does he still have the power to commit suicide? If he is so powerful, how come he has not yet defeated Satan? How can they say God is a man—why can't God be a woman? Dad told me to put my hand down, "This is not school, my lad, you just don't ask questions."

Monday, April 4: No school today since it was Easter Monday. I read an interesting article in the *Montreal Star* about the church's response to the controversial hidden messages found in rock music. The church claims if you played certain rock songs backwards, you'd be able to hear satanic messages. This, in itself, is not new. The article was about the songs of devil-worshipping bands themselves. Normally, their songs sound so awful that it could be easily reproduced by throwing a piece of sheet metal into a thresher."* When they played a song by a certain devil-worshipping band backwards, the church leaders were shocked to hear strange commands, such as, "Brush your

---

* This reflects modern society's contempt of teenager's music. One common complaint is that teenagers' music is so loud that the intensity level of the hiss between songs sound like a 747 jet with muffler problems. The seemingly chaotic, obscene, unintelligible nature of rock music appears to make teenager's brain shrivel to the size of a peanut. If concerned parents listen carefully, they'll hear their son's brain rattling around in his cranium like a BB in a can. At the pounding beat of the music, young fans perform what social anthropologists call, "head-banging." This violent shaking of the head in an up and down manner is performed as if they are trying to shake the said BB out of their nose. If the music is sufficiently loud enough, it can make the head, in an act of self-preservation, eject the entire contents of inner ear where they can land with little parachutes at a safe distance away, such as Siberia.

teeth," "Eat your vegetables," and "Wash behind your ears." While abiding the right to freedom of speech, the church decreed that we are permitted to listen to devil-worshipping music as long as they are played backwards.

I popped over to see Luderick and we went to the schoolyard to play ball hockey. After 45 minutes of taking slap shots on each other, we walked back to his house and discussed his conspiracy of the week: the "Walk/Don't Walk" signal. He has made an intensive study for a school project about the "walk/don't walk" signals at three main intersections downtown and formulated his conclusion: signal always changes to "Don't walk" when you're halfway across the street.

Luderick asserted in his best expert voice, "The purpose here is obviously sinister as this has an effect of inducing undue stress to innocent pedestrians." He paused for effect. When no such effect was forthcoming, he continued, "It makes people think they are about to be run over and this causes them to rush over to the other side. The induction of stress is obviously a government ploy to reduce people's lives and shorter lives mean less pension they have to hand out."

He might have a point.

Tuesday, April 5: At school, Alfonsino's bandages have come off but his skin has a scaly appearance, as if he's growing new skin.

"I got a special cream for this condition, I ordered it from Belgium," he whispered to me when he caught me staring.

Our sexy French teacher Julie Poisson is no longer subbing! Mr. Poisson came back to find his desk, much to his puzzlement, festooned with flowers, boxes of chocolates and slips of paper with phone numbers on them. He turned to the class and said, "*Merci beaucoup, mais je préfère les pommes.*"

I saw Jake strolling out of school with a maroon briefcase with "V.F." stencilled on it. This is odd. He never carries a schoolbag or even a briefcase because he never brings home his homework; his victims do them for him.

What a strange word: "briefcase." There are no briefs and no case of beer.

Molly was on the bus again today—what luck! When I had a crush on her, she was nowhere to be seen and these days I'm seeing her on a daily basis. This time, the university guy wasn't with her; he sat with the same guy he was eyeing last week. She sulked a few rows behind, glaring at the back of his head. When she caught me glancing in her direction, she met my eyes, forced a small smile and looked away.

Despite my misery over losing Demoiselle last week, Mum was ecstatically happy today. She's happy with her new job. She sang and danced as she made delicious homemade zucchini pizza. She told us how much she loves her new job, the responsibilities and the power bestowed to her to command $600 000-year CEOs to sit down and wait for the company president.

Wednesday, April 6: Mr. Fry arrived to class this morning with his papers in a Steinberg's plastic bag.

He looked up to the class and said, "Someone stole my maroon briefcase yesterday. It had the initials 'V.F.' imprinted on the side. If any of you have seen it, please give it back, no questions asked." He was looking at Jake as he said this. The big lug leaned back with a well-practised "Not-me" expression.

I was home alone doing my Latin homework in the living room when the doorbell rang behind me. I wished my hearing aids were off because standing before me when I opened the door was, of all people, Dweeby. He mumbled something in a pleading tone.

"What? Say again?"

More mumble. I strained my ears and maximized my lip-reading ability—the only word I caught was "Ilisha."

"Uh, she doesn't want to see you anymore," I said as I backed up, a construction truck reversing with beeping sounds.

From hearing his whiny burbles and seeing him kneeling with his hands in a prayer position, I deduced that he wasn't trying to sell me encyclopaedias.

"No way," I said. He began to blubber and cry, tears zigzagging down his cratered face. He moaned and mumbled loudly and didn't make sense at all (he never did in the first place). I straightened my back before him and said, "Forget Ilisha. Look for another fish in the sea. She already has a new man in her life now, a guy named Donny."

He stopped his blubbering and frowned at me with intense curiosity.

"Donny Brook?" he mouthed. I read his lips clearly for the first time.

"Uh, yeah."

He jerked up, kicked the porch post and slammed his fist against the wall all the while spitting out several sentences in his version of Swedish-Russian-Yeniseian. He whipped out a sheet of paper, scribbled on it and shoved the note to me. "Donny is my brother. Tell Illisha this: Donny is only using her in a sick game and will dump her like yesterday's newspaper."

He stormed off before I could ask him what he meant by "a sick game."

Friday, April 8: As soon as I arrived home from school, I leafed through the mail—bingo! A letter from Demoiselle! I put it under my pillow and saved it to read in bed tonight.

Zoned out after studying for two straight hours, I was taking a break and plodded into the kitchen to make my classic peanut butter and banana sandwich when, from next to the doorway, a fist flashed out and whoomped me in the shoulder. Snapped awake, my scarecrow body slammed against the wall and a booming voice filled the kitchen. "How's it going, Egg?"

I smiled weakly at Donny. He stood over me, sporting a wide "we-are-tough-buddies-with-barn-door-shoulders" smile. Again!

"Fine," I mumbled, rubbing my shoulder and regretted I didn't put on my spiked epaulets. I'm going to get this guy for the bruise-tattoos he's giving me. The school officials are suspicious and have been asking me questions about my home situation.

While I made my sandwich, my parents came in and talked to him with a sickening level of enthusiasm. When they finally went upstairs and Donny was waiting for Ilisha alone, I made my move. I snuck up to him, put my face into his and whispered, "Hey, I got news for you. Your brother was here this afternoon."

"Doing what?" he snapped, his eyes bulging.

"What do you think?" I said, preferring to leave it to his imagination.

He grunted, grabbed his truck keys and slammed the door on his way out.

Ilisha came down to be greeted by an empty living room.

"Donny left. He had some business to take care of," I kindly informed her.

"Damn. I'll have to go to the volleyball game by myself," she said.

A whole new game will be played soon.

Saturday, April 9: Last night I read Demoiselle's letter while lying comfortably in bed. With trembling hands and beating heart, I read her letter.

Dear Egbert,

Thank you for writing to me. I'm fine! I enjoyed reading your funny letter! I laughed when you wrote that sea otters don't live in St. Lawrence River because they can never find a vacant one-bedroom apartment! No, I don't know where light goes when you turn it off. You write good. You wrote a lot! I'm in Secondary 5 like you. I hate math!

I tried call you. A strange man answered and hung up to me. Maybe I gotten wrong number. Ugh! Yes, I liked dance with you. You look nice. I have two brothers. One is 22 and the other is 20. I'm 17 too. I wake up at 6:45. I hate waking up!

Yours fondly, Demoiselle XXXOOO

It was written on a small sheet of pink paper with flowers adorning the edges and bore a faint scent of her perfume. It smelled so fresh; it brought back memories of us dancing. She made little hearts over the "i"s and drew a silly face next to my name. It didn't matter to me that her letter was short, full of grammatical errors and "Dick-and-Jane-ish." I can scarcely believe she wrote back!

I spent the morning before Mrs. Tautog's speech lesson writing and re-writing a W.O. Mitchell literary prize-worthy letter and even included a poem in the style of Leonard Cohen. After all, she did say I write well, so I've to keep up to her high standards. I felt good again, the heavy clouds of doubt and despondency have passed by and I've climbed out my dank pit, the warm sun shining upon my smiling face.

While I was connecting with Demoiselle, Donny and Ilisha disconnected! They had a fantastic screaming match late last night at the door as I ate my snack. This morning she was crying at the kitchen table and was being consoled by Mum. She spent the rest of the afternoon listening to the classic country music album, "*She Got The Gold Mine And I Got The Shaft.*"

Throwing a barrier to dam the surge of guilt, I rationalized by telling myself that I protected her from being used by this jock. However, an annoying tinny voice in the deep recesses of my mind added, "If Dweeby is right about his brother."

The spring dance will be in exactly two weeks!

I watched a good game on "*Hockey Night in Canada.*" The Montreal Canadiens crushed the Pittsburgh Penguins 9–1!

Sunday, April 10: I went over to Luderick's place after lunch. He had returned from his usual Sunday church mass and was still in his spiffy Sunday suit. He changed to his usual casual garb while I waited. He came out of his bedroom, tucking in his AC/DC T-shirt and said, "Here, come and see what I did to my alarm clock." He showed me his modified clock—the snooze button was ripped out.

"This button is scourge of society, a social evil," he breathlessly explained. "By allowing people to sleep for an extra ten minutes at a simple press of a button, it gives an endless supply of second chances. Let's say Joe Moe is wakened at his appointed time and doesn't want to get up right away, so he presses the snooze button. Ten minutes later, still sleepy, he presses the damn button again and again and again. This goes on until Joe has slept 40 minutes past the time he was supposed to get up. So he jumps out of bed, skips breakfast, backs into a couple of garbage cans and runs over a squirrel. And this is before he gets into his car. He's late for work and his boss fires him. He racks up huge debts, his wife divorces him, the bank takes his home and finally he becomes alcoholic, votes N.D.P. and dies in the gutter."

"The innocent-looking snooze button is responsible for $1 billion in lost productivity and a host of health-related ailments associated with skipping breakfast."

He took a deep breath and continued, "It teaches I-will-do-it-later irresponsibility. Since time moves forward and there's no going back, we have only one chance of doing something. The snooze button creates an illusion that the world will always give you a second chance."

Luderick went on to explain how this is related to a phenomenon he calls, "The Elvis factor." He brought up a fact: when famous people die, their value increases dramatically. When Elvis went to the great big gig in the sky, sales of his recordings shot up and more money have been made with the

Elvis name than when he was alive.

"When he died, people realized they could no longer see or hear him alive again. They felt they were denied a second chance to see him, so they compensate by re-creating him again in their minds. How? By buying corny Elvis memorabilia, reading trashy stories of Elvis sightings and attending endless Elvis impersonation shows. People are so spoiled with second chances that they want to believe."

Luderick went on to expound about how TV re-runs, library loan grace periods, credit cards and movie sequels were additional social evils perpetuating this misguidance.

Suffice to say, this lecture was enough to make me take Burundian language classes and I excused myself.

While I was making my peanut butter and banana sandwich at home, I saw Ilisha, lying deep in the sofa, listening to more depressing country songs, including the classic, "Don't Know Whether To Kill Myself Or Go Bowling." She stared at the ceiling with a faraway look, eyes wet and her foot moving rhythmically to the music. She has even forfeited her daily morning jog and taken to sleeping in and skipping classes. Someone get this girl a new boyfriend, preferably a WWII relic plane pilot.

Monday, April 11: I dropped Demoiselle's letter in the mailbox on my way to the bus stop. For some odd reason, an image of Molly's sultry face came to mind. Huh? What's going on here?

Jake nearly pushed Mr. Fry over the edge because he was up to his usual class-disrupting tricks. Today, he made animal sounds every time Mr. Fry said, "Sheep." After the twelfth "Baaaa" from the back of the class, Mr. Fry stopped mid-sentence and rushed up to the Neanderthal, his face beet-red. He wagged a short stubby finger at Jake and, lips trembling at a 6.5 on the Richter scale, stammered, "You, you...." Jake slowly removed his heavy feet from Alfonsino's desk and stood up over him. The teacher found himself looking at Jake's enormous stomach. Can you guess what the brave teacher said?

"Uh, sit down," he mustered feebly. Of all angry, invective, forceful words available in the dictionary, Mr. Fry picks "sit" and "down." He returned to his place in front of the class and continued to teach us about sheep bacteriophages. Jake sat down slowly, put his feet back on Alfonsino's desk and smirked with a goofy grin.

When I came home, no one was there and I began my essay for English lit. I went into Mum and Dad's bedroom to look for spare loose-leaf paper and I spied something in the corner of the room: a plastic bag hidden between Mum's dresser and the wall. When curiosity was sufficient to overwhelm me but kept the cat alive, I looked in. Staring at its contents, my eyebrows furrowed enough to knit a pair of socks. Nestled inside the bag were several pens, erasers, markers, staplers and nameplates. Examining the items closely, I recognized, to my shock, that they were all office supplies from "Monopoly Conglomerate Corporation Company, Inc."! Mum stole them!

I had a flashback: I'm walking down a dim stairway towards a room filled with colourful lights. At the bottom of the stairs, I see a dead tree with assorted junk hanging from its branches. A Christmas tree. At the left of the tree, I see a single bulging sock tacked to the mantelpiece. I eagerly looked inside and saw what Santa had left me: packing peanuts from the bottom of his bag.

Wrong flashback.

This was the correct flashback, complete with fuzzy edges on the screen: Mum comes home, crying. She sits me down at the kitchen table and tells me she lost her beloved hairdressing job because she was caught stealing several hairbrushes and tubes of facial cream.

Fade back to reality. If her Genghis Stalin Hitler Pinochet-boss finds out, she will lose her new job! I want to confront her but am in a Catch 22 situation. If I tell Mum what I found, she'll strangle me for being in their room because I'm strictly forbidden from going there. If I don't tell her, I'll be safe but she'll risk losing her job. What should I do?

Wednesday, April 13: Mr. Fry showed us a film about stick insects. I hate it when teachers show documentary films in class even if it's a break from listening to monotonous lectures. Teachers take forever to set up the movie projector*, I've no clue what the narrator is saying and if the teacher explains something, he's doing it from the back next to the projector. Plus, it's always too dark to read lips. I hope it won't be on the exam.

A shocking university scandal broke open today—five hockey players from the St. Coregon Cougars were involved in a "sex scoring" game with local women. Each player was given points for every woman they boinked. It was based on a graduated system: if the guy passes the centre line (equivalent to 1st base), he gets five points; if he crosses the blue line, he gets ten points and if he shoots and scores, he gets 25 points. By the end of the season, the player with the most points gets

---

* An intensive 6-month course on movie projector fumbling is taught at all teaching schools and Mr. Fry, according to his academic records, was top of his class. The course teaches such aspects as, "Threading the film leader through the projector with thick Siberian mitts", "Looking for the 'on' switch in the dark without being electrocuted", and most difficult of them all, "Putting lint in the lens to create the effect of dancing pieces of hair on the screen." Today. technology and modernism have replaced this antiquated course with "VCR fumbling" where professors are taught to insert salami sandwiches into the machine. DVD fumbling courses was made available recently; one module taught them how to use the nifty coffee cup holder.

the money jackpot. Get this—this is the team Donny plays for.

When Mum and Dad left to go shopping, I snuck into their room to check on Mum's bag of office supplies—more things! In addition to more pens and paper clips, she also collected three company light bulbs, two small plants and six coffee mugs with different names on them and a roll of toilet paper. I decided to risk my neck and confront her about her recent stockpiling. However, it's 10:30 p.m. and she and Dad have not arrived home yet. I'll go to bed and confront her tomorrow after school so I would no longer be distracted by these illicit events and stop accidentally brushing my teeth with Dad's athlete's foot ointment.

Demoiselle should be getting my letter any time soon.

Thursday, April 14: Mum neglected to wake me up this morning and I was 45 minutes late for school. I tried to evoke the "Deaf pity" card with the secretary into not giving me detention but my tears failed me. I had to stay after school for two hours and the punishment was to sit with arms folded and do nothing but stare at the clock on Headmaster Sculpin's desk. If he catches us so much as to glance away, he would tack on another five minutes to the punishment.

I was amply rewarded for my punishment, if there is such a thing: I met Molly on my way to the bus stop! I was rounding the corner of Maurice Richard St. when I spied her. She was wearing black high-heeled boots, short plaid skirt and half unbuttoned blouse on this warm day. Man, was she ever hot! She strutted up to me, her boobs bouncing.

"Hi there, going to the bus stop?" Her full lips formed the words sensually.

I, the goof, nodded like Gilligan would've if Ginger invited him inside her hut. We walked down the street and she talked a mile-a minute. To my damn luck, a puttering street-cleaning truck was right behind us throughout. The roar of spinning bristles drowned out her words, as lovely they may have been. I would ask her random questions to keep her talking so she wouldn't see that I was drawing a big, fat blank. Plus, walking and reading lips at the same time was dangerous: I had to keep one eye on her lips and the other for the assorted lampposts, parking metres and skinny sidewalk trees waiting to whack me silly. We arrived at the bus stop unscathed but she had to leave immediately.

"Oh—I forgot! I have to go to meet a friend—sorry Eggie. Nice talking to you, you're cute." She kissed her two fingers and planted them on my cheek. My face went hot.

"Ok, hope to see you soon," I croaked. As she sauntered away, I cautiously surveyed the surroundings for Demoiselle. After all, she does live nearby.

After a supper of leftovers by myself, I became so absorbed with homework and my encounter with Molly that I forgot to confront Mum about her pilfered office supplies. She is already in bed as I write this. Tomorrow, I will do it.

Friday, April 15: The St. Coregon University dean issued a report identifying the guilty players of the sex-scoring scandal and has suspended the players indefinitely. One of the players is...cue the drum solo...Donny Brook! We were agog. Ilisha professed no knowledge of this sex scoring game and claimed they've only kissed a few times (that was five points for him).

"We're finished, that's for sure," Ilisha said, making the same "safe" sign she used with Dweeby. I awarded myself 50 points for preventing Donny from gaining any more points with her. The spectre of guilt has faded and my arm no longer shoots out in a psychosomatic spasms. This was becoming dangerous on crowded busses.

Bad news—Mum lost her job. According to her, she was fired because she put a decimal point in the wrong place on the accounting sheet. I know the real reason behind her dismissal but didn't tell Dad because he abhors kleptomaniacs since his last experience with one left him without his pants. (Author's note: I think his father was referring to the plants in his office.)

As dispiriting as this situation is, I have to admire her boss' creativity in firing her, however cruel. He made the whole office, including Mum, take a Morse code class in the morning with a far-fetched explanation that it would be an emergency method of communication if all phones became inoperable. A few hours after the class, the boss hired a large plane to repeatedly pass in between the sun and the office building to send Mum a message. When she noticed the room alternating between light and darkness and saw it was the same plane each time, she wrote down the series of long and short periods of darkness and translated them into Morse code. It read as: refireddoraflounderyoua. She performed mental gymnastics that could've won her a silver medal at the 1980 Olympics and deciphered it. It read, "Dora Flounder you are fired." Her triumph in solving the puzzle was quickly replaced by disappointment.

Mum complained she will have to go back to the awful, dank, depressing employment office which has a happy face sticker on the front door saying, "Come in!"

Saturday, April 16: While doing my biology homework, I became philosophical. Since the body is an aggregate of many parts, I can conceptualize my body on many levels. I can think of it in terms of limbs, fingers, toes, hair and fingernails with dirt under it. I can think of it in terms of organs: skin, muscles and bones. I can think of it in terms of cells that occupy each organ: blood cells, cochlear hair cells and brain cells.

We each have trillions of cells and each cell is made up of a hundred trillion atoms. Each molecule, cell, muscle, or foot, on its own, doesn't a body make, but when they all stick to each other in the proper configuration, it forms into what we call "the body."

What blew me away was this thought: I'm a walking set of bazillions of atoms holding on to each other for dear life! It's a wonder how I manage to stay together without losing a several trillion atoms in my shoulder and having my arm fall off.

"Egg," Dad said in exasperation. "All the molecules in your body are held together by the forces of adhesion like nuclear forces, electromagnetism and gravitational attraction. These forces are what holds everything together."

I wonder what the universe would be without this adhesion? Would anything exist? Would have the universe formed at all? Could there be a planet with intelligent life without this adhesion? Would the beings exist as a cloud of gnats, taking on a rough shape of things? How would they shake hands? How would they eat? What would happen to them if they visited earth?

For her part, Mrs. Tautog only pursed her wrinkly lips at my questions during today's lesson and made me practise pronouncing "adhesion" several times. She never answers my questions.

When I went downstairs a few hours ago, I saw Mum lying on the sofa, the TV flickering upon her vacant eyes and pallid face. A corpse looks more cheerful than this. I tried cheering her up with her favourite phrases: "What goes down, must come up", "When the world hands you a lemon, make Yugos" and "Every cloud has a silver spoon in its mouth." She said nothing. I went back upstairs without another word.

Damn—why didn't I warn her? I felt like crap. But, even if I did, would it have made a difference?

Exactly a week from now is the dance! I can't wait to see Demoiselle again, even though I've not yet received a response from her. I thought about the dreamy night I met her and re-read and smelled her letter.

Sunday, April 17: Mum watched TV all day in the dim basement again. After six hours, she's still down there, bleary eyed and pale, surrounded by stale pizza crusts and empty soft drink cans. She has been watching, *"One-pin bowling championship tournament for the cross-eyed."*

Since my brain was devoted to Demoiselle for the past few days, I've been neglecting my homework. I spent all day catching up, working on my science paper, tomorrow's public speaking class and other assignments. I had to find a way to tell Luderick that I can't see him to discuss his conspiracy of the week. Since my parents weren't home, I had to call him by myself. I switched my hearing aid into the "telephone" mode, dialed and waited for a good five minutes for someone to answer. Strange—I didn't hear anything, not even a ring. I hung up and decided to pay him a surprise visit on Wednesday.

Monday, April 18: Mum slept all night in her mole's hole in the basement with the TV on and shuffled into the kitchen this morning, her baggy dark eyes sunken in her skull. Her skin was greyish pale and her lips dried and cracked. I wanted to make a joke about Halloween being too early, but I held my tongue. Not a good joke to say to a walking dead before her first cup of coffee. It was a relief to see that she has returned to her somewhat normal self by late afternoon—she was scaring the cat.

We had oral presentation in Mr. Bonito's class today and this time I was prepared. After Jake's speech on 16th century torture devices in Latvia, I explained (i.e., croaked) the top ten reasons why we didn't evolve to have eyes in the back of our heads.

I scored 80% on this speech even though we were supposed to talk about Latvian culture. With slow, measured words to use up the five minutes of allotted time, Alfonsino talked about a farmer who claimed he had extracted the chemical that can make a pig's tail curl because, at the time, all pigs' tails were straight. The farmer first tested the product on his head and ended up looking like the business end of a toilet brush. When the product became well known, a bed manufacturer became interested and bought the recipe for the chemical extract to make bedsprings. Despite his pitiful efforts, Alfonsino was given a surprising 71% because he made repeated emphasis that the farmer was from Latvia.

While waiting for my bus, I saw tiny Mr. Fry drive by in a huge light blue 1970s American car. No more Austin Mini. Overcompensation? Other than that, Molly was nowhere to be seen. Wait—who does my heart belong to—sexy, out-of-my-league Molly or demure Demoiselle?

Dad made an appointment for me to see a Dr. Greyling tomorrow afternoon as part of an annual ritual I go through. It's nothing really to do with checking my health, looking for fatal diseases or to feel my balls a mite too long. It's only to get any doctor to fill out the income tax disabilities claim form to prove to the ten-watt government that I've a permanent disability. It's something we have to do each year, "in event of any changes." We cannot get it through their collective brains that I can't become hearing one year and hearing impaired the next and become hearing again, like a light switch. Permanent is permanent. At least the appointment will excuse me from school after lunch.

Tuesday, April 19: I saw Mum dressed up at the breakfast table, which was an improvement over the corpse on the sofa downstairs.

"I'm goin' to the employment office wit' Mora, Egg. Don't forget yer doctor's appointment."

I left school after lunch and took the bus to Dr. Greyling's office today. While I waiting for the bus, I saw a familiar huge light blue 1970s American car drive by but Mr. Fry wasn't in the driver's seat—it was Jake. I thought his driver's licence was suspended back in December for his attempt to run down Alfonsino. I arrived at the doctor's office and after seeing the secretary, I took a number and entered a large waiting room filled with haggard mothers with sniffling children, depressed senior citizens and late-season ski bums with broken limbs. An entire family of Israelites sat silently in a corner. As I was about to sit in the only seat near the secretary, a rude old lady with blue hair pushed me aside and plopped there. I ended up sitting next to a tattooed biker guy with a leather vest in the far corner. He had number 66. Mine was 89. I selected the biggest issue of Canadian Aviation, turned up the volume of my hearing aid and prepared to wait. And did I ever wait. Each time a number was called, I perked up my ears but it was difficult to comprehend the garbled voice on the intercom. An hour and half later, I became fed up with waiting and approached the secretary.

"Did you call number 89 yet?"

"I called it about 20 minutes ago. Take another number and go into the waiting room."

"I'm hearing impaired. I didn't hear the damn number. Can you please come into the room and tell me when my number is called?" She agreed, although reluctantly. I trudged back into the room of sniffles, long faces and limbs in white casts.

I sat where I could see the secretary around the corner and dared not to take any bathroom breaks or read any magazines for the next hour. When the secretary finally called my number, I went straight into the doc's office. My examination by Dr. Greyling was something else. I've heard that out of seven-odd years in medical school training, the total amount of time they explain hearing impairment is 45 minutes. Dr. Greyling must've been sleeping in class the day they taught this.

When I entered his office, I found a wizened old man with shocking white hair sitting behind a cheap and pockmarked desk. Two dead ferns hung from the ceiling by the window in the corner. A bad sign. There's a saying: "Don't accept advice from a doctor who has dead plants in his office."

Without looking up, he spent several minutes reading my file and said, "Ah, he's hearing impaired." He proceeded to exaggerate his lip movements as if I had visual problems. I could smell his Surströmming lunch ten paces away. I gave him the form and he asked me the usual questions:

"How long have you been hearing impaired?"

"Are you able to dress yourself independently?"

"Does it interfere with your daily bowel movements?"

After hearing a few of my replies, he looked up and asked, "Your accent—are you French?"

"No, sir."

"Do you have a sore throat?"

"No, sir, this is how I speak."

He wrote notes in my file and, after directing me to the little examination room, he gave the standard medical exam. When he examined my ears with his otoscope, he took special interest in them normally reserved for coroners examining a murder victim. He finally remarked, "There is solid pink matter there."

I took out my hearing aids and asked him to look again.

"Ah, better now." He took a long time to probe my ear canal, pulling on my ears this way and that. In a brief moment of patronizing humour, he stuck the otoscope in my ear and turned his face to me and mouthed, "Hey look, the light is coming out the other side!"

I gave the barest smile.

Once he was done, he wrote notes in my file.

One other problem was the eye exam. After I put my hearing aids back in, he told me to take off my glasses and turned out the lights. A Snellen eye chart was projected upon the office wall and I faintly heard his raspy voice emanating from the darkness.

"What? Again please."

He repeated the same mumble, but only slightly louder.

"I still don't understand you. It's dark in here."

A deep sigh came from the darkness and he grabbed my hand and slapped it over my right eye.

"Read mumble mumble," he said next to my ears.

I gave it my best shot and read the first line. More

mumbling. I read the next line. Mumble. And so on. He grabbed my left hand and slapped it over my other eye. Same thing again: mumble and read lines. He finally turned on the lights and wrote more notes in my file, appearing concerned. I put my glasses back on.

"Wait here," he mouthed and shuffled into the next room, returning with a small bottle.

"Take off your glasses, I'm going to give you eye drops," his mouth enunciated each word with wide lips. I sat back and he dropped milky liquid in my eyes that effectively blurred my vision for the next five minutes. He gave a long rambling explanation and still expected me to read his lips through the hazy vision in front of me. I had no clue what he said. He wrote something on a small notepad and by then, my vision cleared.

"This is a prescription is for your blocked nose. It's important you follow the directions. This tax form is for your parents," he said as he handed me the papers.

When I was about to leave, he said, "Wait—I almost forgot. I need to give you something else." He went back into the other room.

"Here, use this for now," he said as he put the item into my hands. It was a walking stick for the blind. I gave it to the ski bum on my way out. Maybe it will help him find trees.

At the drugstore, I was approaching the prescription counter when the same rude old lady with blue hair shuffled in front of me, cutting me off. I had to wait ten minutes while she babbled with the pharmacist in French and when I finally gave my prescription, I was told to sit aside and wait (more waiting!). After about 15 minutes, I heard what sounded like my name being called and at the same time, the rude old lady with blue hair was about to cut in again but, with youth on my side, I took several long strides and stepped in front of her.

"My turn," I told her with a smug smile. She pursed her wrinkly lips and returned to her seat. The pharmacist looked at me in a funny way and said, "I have your prescription." She took out a long tube out of a box and instructed, "Insert this tube gently up to the halfway mark with a twisting motion and squeeze once. It should be done every night right before bedtime until the tube is finished."

11:23 pm. I came back from the hospital a few minutes ago. Mum found me with half of a 4-inch long tube sticking out of my nose and took me to the hospital to get it removed.

Mum was half-upset, half-amused and she asked over and over, "Egg, what on earth were you doing putting a vaginal tube up your silly nose?"

I just thought of something—I wonder what the old woman will do with my nasal spray?

Wednesday, April 20: I looked through today's mail for a letter from Demoiselle—nothing. I'm getting worried. The dance is three days away and we've not made the connection. How do I know how she feels about me? Was it what they call a one-night stand? Should I risk blowing my cover and call her? The questions are raking my brain over hot coals.

I went over to see Luderick after supper. His mother complained she heard a long obscene message on her answering machine on Sunday. She had to listen to five minutes of heavy breathing that sounded like an elephant after jumping on a trampoline.

"Is this whatis the world coming to? Obscene messages on the answering machine?" I took interest in the ceiling and didn't answer.

Once we were out of earshot in his room, Luderick grumbled, "God, man, my mother made me stay in church ALL afternoon because she had to pray for forgiveness for listening to the whole phone message. I was so freaking bored."

He was quiet today, staring into space with occasional comments while I looked though the Penthouse magazines he hides under the mattress. The only interesting comment he made was that every time he shook hands with a public official, his watch disappeared and the deficit would be lowered by 50 dollars the next day. He also morosely mumbled something about being depressed. After looking through his third Penthouse mag, he made me go home early.

"What's up, Luderick?" I asked.

He explained that he has been feeling increasingly helpless and powerless with each new conspiracy he discovers. His forlorn eyes staring vacantly into space, he said, "I alone cannot fight the monopolistic, imperialistic, dictatorship system of the government and the multi-national corporations on top of that. How can I be happy living within the greedy, capitalist, money-comes-first nature of our corrupt society?"

I was surprised at his language. Usually young people don't sprout such revolutionary words until they're in university, or at least, old enough to make macaroni and cheese in their own apartment.

I told Dad about Luderick's comments and he thinks my friend was talking about his mother being the oppressive force. Hmmm—that was an excellent point.

Thursday, April 21: I saw an interesting article in the newspaper this morning. A teen my age named Frederick made a spectacular failed suicide attempt last night. To ensure success, the guy tied a rope around his neck to an overhanging tree, drank poison and held a gun to his head while standing on an edge of a cliff. As he jumped off, the shot missed and the bullet cut through the rope. He fell into the lake below that was so chemically polluted that the water acted as an emetic and this prevented the poison from working. He was rescued and brought into a boat against his will by two fishermen. As they approached the shore, the guy tried to jump off the boat in another suicide attempt but was conked out with a fish club. The teen is presently "resting comfortably" at the Lakeshore General Hospital.

Upon arriving at school, I saw Mr. Fry on a green bicycle wheeling down St. Jacques Avenue. So odd to see a teacher on a bike! Stranger still, was seeing him waiting with me at the bus stop after school, looking hot and bothered. Before our bus pulled up, I spotted Jake with a big goofy grin pedaling, with his knees sticking out east and west, a green bike. Mr. Fry didn't see this.

I looked in the mailbox again. The mailbox was empty as the space between Bobby Clark's teeth. I'm beginning to feel like a balding man who wore a wig that made him look like he has less hair.

I stopped by the bookstore and bought a recently released big book on Spitfire planes. It has everything: the engine specs, gripping true tales of air battles, famous pilots and prints of full-colour action paintings. Ilisha told Mum that I blew $45 on the book.

"This is a waste o' money, Egg," Mum groaned. "You'll need to save fer college."

"It *is* for college, Mum. Every would-be pilot should own this book, you know."

She looked at me, sighed and changed the topic.

"Oh Egg, you 'ave an appointment wit' Dr. Albacore for an hearin' test, your audiogram is too old. We need to send a new one for the taxes." Great—another doctor.

With three assignments and an English literature paper due tomorrow, I picked up the Spitfire book. I was so absorbed in the harrowing tales of air combat I scarcely noticed time flying by. It was 1:17 a.m. and I had done nothing for homework. After deliberating between being charged four detentions (one for each missed assignment) or working all night and getting no sleep at all, I took the wise scholarly course of action. I put my schoolbooks on my desk, sharpened my pencils, rolled up my sleeves and went to bed. I'll wake up at 4 a.m. tomorrow to do it.

Friday, April 22: Mum woke me up at the same time as usual and I did my homework on the bouncing bus. Mr. Acipenser complained about my "chicken scratch handwriting" seen in my Latin homework.

The weather was wonderful today: high whipping winds and cold rain falling on the piles of dark-coloured mush of dejected leftover snow that have been resisting all attempts to melt. Mr. Barracuda took this as a good day for us to play rugby on the school fields where the grass is still gone and is due back from their trip to Florida. This decision betrayed his "9-1-1-hangs-up-every-time-I-call" misery. Jake loves rugby but he pretty much plays by himself because 99% of the class don't want the ball. We would throw it to the nearest victim before Jake could crush us but we weren't always successful. If you look carefully at the field next to Canterbury, you'll see ground imprints of squashed students that look not unlike contorted snow angels.

Alfonsino bragged today to anyone who would listen that he has "bagged a date" for tomorrow's dance. "You shoulda seen me, I strolled up to this chick at Dorval Shops and asked her out just like that. She fluttered her eyes and said, 'Sure, handsome.' Man, I gotta try that more often!"

I went to see Dr. Albacore the audiologist after school for my hearing test. He's a mad-scientist prototype: white lab coat, thick glasses, unshaven face and wild mane of hair he could only achieve by sticking a screwdriver in a wall socket.

"Ah, there you are Mr. Flounder," he squinted at me and slowly motioned me towards the testing booth. "I'll now conduct my experiment." It was the same drill for the last ten years of my life: I sit in a sound-proof booth with walls so thick that if an H-bomb was dropped on Ste. Catherine Street, I wouldn't hear it. He puts these tight and heavy headphones over my ears and instructs me to press a button each time I hear a beep, "No matter how soft." He also reads from a list of words with his mouth covered and I repeat what I heard. This tests my "speech discrimination," even though I don't have anything against speech impediments.

He gave me a copy of my hearing test results and made the same joke he does every time: he puts his hand on my shoulder and in a regretful tone, says, "I'm sorry to tell you this but you're hearing impaired." He smiles and perks up, "See you next time!" and walks away laughing.

Still no letter from Demoiselle. At this point, I don't mind. The dance is tomorrow and seeing Demoiselle again would be much better than getting a piece of paper from her.

What a genius I am! I thought of a creative way to avenge my sister's tattle-tailing to Mum about me buying the Spitfire book. While Ilisha was away, I found leftover concrete powder and sprinkled it liberally into her hairdryer. The hairdryer will blow the plaster on her wet hair and voila! Instant white plastered hair! I chuckled to myself as I placed the hairdryer back under the sink.

The dance is tomorrow night!

Saturday, April 23: Eagerly awaiting results from the act of vengeance against my enemy sister, I woke up early and slowly ate breakfast. An hour earlier, I saw her sleepwalk into the bathroom for her morning shower.

"She'll snap awake after she blow-dries her hair," I thought to myself, sniggering.

As I ate my breakfast, I upped my hearing aids and soon enough, I heard her stomping down the steps. I could barely keep myself from giggling and kept my eyes riveted to my Dino-Pebbles cereal. She charged into the kitchen and I, ready to give a look innocent enough to acquit Idi Amin Dada, glanced at her. Her hair—her hair was...normal?

It was perfect, blond, shiny and luxurious. Not a speck of white plaster.

I gulped.

"What's wrong, Egg?" She asked.

Next, Mum enters the kitchen. I inspected her hair from the corner of my eyes—normal.

I gulped again.

I closed my eyes and said to myself, "Oh please, please, please. Don't let this happen again."

Sure enough, Dad walks in, his face annoyed and his hair whiter than snow and styled as if an elephant sneezed in his face.

"Bloody hell, Ilisha, I use your hairdryer once in my life

and my hair didn't come out right."

"It doesn't look that bad, Dad," Ilisha said. "I can fix it."

Journal, it did look bad. He looks as if he's running at "Six million dollar man" speed while sitting still and eating porridge in his bathrobe.

When Dad answered the door to Mrs. Tautog, she gave him a startled look. "Oh my, looks like someone has been riding a motorcycle without a helmet." Since I was going to meet Demoiselle tonight, I practised extra hard on my "s", "isp" and "tch" sounds.

I'm back from the dance and have bad news—Demoiselle wasn't there! After all the buildup and anticipation, I never felt so disappointed. I spent a good while preparing for the dance: I showered, dressed, combed my hair over my hearing aids and ate non-gassy food. Dad drove me there and I was one of the first people to arrive. I sat in the hallway near the entrance and watched people come in. Alfonsino came in with a date with a bad make-up job and an ill-fitting red dress. As they passed by, the girl winked at me and I laughed—it was Luderick in my sister's dress!

As each group of people entered, my eyes would light up like cheesy Christmas lights, half expecting to see my love. Fifty minutes of Christmas light-blinking later, no Demoiselle. The clock inched towards the hour before the doors were to be closed for the night as they don't allow anyone in after 8 p.m. My head snapped towards the door every time it made the slightest movement. Two minutes before eight o'clock, the security guy came by and locked the door. I vehemently protested this early closing. The burly guy stood there, listened and said nothing. After I pleaded, cajoled and offered him a small role in a movie about bodyguards, he looked at his watch and said, "Two minutes have gone. It's now eight o'clock."

The hair on my forearms wanted to drag my arms to his thick neck and strangle him. At this point, I told myself that it was possible that she did come in but I didn't recognize her. Buoyed by this optimistic idea, I searched everywhere for her, but didn't see her. However, I did see Alfonsino screaming and running out of the bathroom with his remaining hair engulfed in flames. Luderick stood by, trying his best to suppress his laughter with gloved hands. This only distracted me of my pain and disappointment for a brief few seconds. I called off my search, plodded outside and waited for her on the cold steps. After waiting two hours in vain, I dejectedly stood up and left with a feeling of profound emptiness. I walked around under the stillness of the night and misty streetlights until Dad arrived to pick me up.

Sunday, April 24: I woke up this morning feeling lost and confused. All day I felt like a cheap after-dinner mint in a greasy roadside restaurant (things must be worse than I thought—I'm starting to use bad analogies.)

I stayed in my bed all morning, wallowing in my thoughts and feeling the comfortable numbness of depression. If she was fond of me, why didn't she show up? Did she change her mind about me? Was it something I said in the letter to her? To remove myself from the pain of an unrequited love, I stopped the noise in my head and stared into the indefinable space in front of me. Faces of girls I once liked floated into the silent room above me, wavering and blending with the colours of emotions associated with each face: Panga in kindergarten, Tilapia my deaf grade 5 sweetheart, Molly the bus rebel, the valley girl, the neighbour girl with the overbite and now, Demoiselle. Strips of cold reality merged with swirls of multi-coloured tapestry of fantasy, stirring and stirring around in the chaotic flowing brook. Emerging from beneath the bridge, the coloured swirls recede farther and farther around sharp rocks and trees, its many fingers twisting and bubbling. A lone fish struggled upstream, gasping and fighting the current. Forlorn and alone, I stand afar upon the wooden bridge despondently watching the receding colours; the bridge leads me in one direction and the memories swirl away in another.

I think I do my best writing while suffering from the blues so this could be a good thing. Since I was so poetically muddled and depressed, I didn't see Luderick today for our usual Sunday meeting, although I was eager to know how his "date" went last night. Next week, I will. I lolled in bed and tried to muster interest in the new Spitfire book. All I could think of are those Asian kamikaze pilots, ending their lives for the war cause (and why did they wear helmets, anyway?).

Even though the Latin homework is due tomorrow, I didn't bother cracking open the book because I didn't care at all. Mum and I spent the night watching a TV movie about a half-blind hunter and his petrified dog. Dad didn't notice my depression; he stayed in his den and read, *Analysis of Assorted Italian Reactions After Sitting on a Tack.*

Monday, April 25: I dragged myself to school on this drizzly morning. Bill Bream told me how Alfonsino's hair caught on fire at the dance. Alfonsino was fixing what was left of his pompadour in front of the bathroom mirror. Fixing his hair is something he does 25 times a day and this in itself constitutes a harmless activity. Akin to piercing your cheek with a fork, no matter how much experience a person has doing something, he or she will screw up at least once. What Alfonsino did wrong was lighting a cigarette and using the hair spray at the same time. Having a brain case that echoes when he talks, he didn't know that his hair spray was flammable. Like the "Suggested serving" advice on cereal boxes, he thought the "flammable" warning symbol on the can was a demonstration of a possible hairstyle that could be achieved by using the spray. All it took was a strong spritz of hair spray and a flick of his jumbo lighter to remove all doubt about his lack of intelligence. After bouncing around outside the bathroom, he put out the flames by sticking his head in a toilet bowl. One of the many lessons he needs to learn: check the symbol on the washroom door before entering, even if your hair is on fire. Hiding under his mother's makeup, I could see the black eye one big girl gave him.

"Did you get the load of date, though? Alfonsino needs glasses—it was so obvious it was a guy!" Bill exclaimed.

With most of his hair gone, students are calling him "Peanut head" Alfonsino. He doesn't mind this nickname, a welcomed change from being called, "Moo-alf" and "Three-nipple Alfie."

Bill Bream also told me that last night, Jake was caught driving erratically and was pulled over by the police on suspicion of drinking and driving. He was in a large American car that was registered as stolen. The officer made him walk the white line to prove his sobriety. When he failed the test miserably, he told the constable that he couldn't walk straight because he had a glass eye. Suspecting the big doofus was lying, the constable asked him, "Which eye is the glass one?" He answered, "Both of them."

I drew detention for not doing the Latin assignment. Who gives a hoot?

Under dark clouds, I turned the corner to my no. 90 bus stop and, lo and behold, standing there was Molly! My heart quickening, I strolled up to her but stopped short when I saw her talking to another guy. Not wanting to be a third wheel, I kept my back to her until the bus arrived. I braved a backward glance only to see an empty space and my stomach sank. What is going on with me? Do I reach for the girl drifting away or chase after an elusive dream like an idiot?

I'm still agonizing over being stood up by Demoiselle. Why is it a bowl of plump, juicy, cherries for other people and a bowl of inedible plastic ones for me? You know, you see a bowl of what resembles perfect, delicious fruit and being ravenous, you reach out to pluck one but find it fake. You feel both disappointed and foolish in one shot.

Wednesday, April 27: It was during Mr. Fry's lecture about how most bees spend their entire lives without ever finding a mate when I made a big decision. It's the biggest, boldest and most unprecedented decision in my life. Here it is: I've decided to call Demoiselle and ask her out. I've never went out on a date and being deaf as a snake, this is a big move, you see. My mounting anxiety prompted me to decide to call her before she forgets about me and joins a basket-weaving commune. Since the phone is as useful for me as roller blades for drunken giraffes, the only way I can call her is through my mother. I'll have her talk to Demoiselle on the phone while I stand nearby, telling her what to say. I know this is at par with having your mother buy you Care Bears pyjamas, I don't want to give Demoiselle an impression I'm a dolt who asks stupid questions such as, "If a piece of meat is very lean, will it tip over?"

The only catch is that I'll have to explain it to Mum and hope she can keep a straight face. Typically, if I mention anything remotely associated with "girl", "date" or "love", her face would excitedly wobble around like a training pilot in a strong wind tunnel and say, "Oooohhh, Egg's got a crush on a girl?" If I don't stop her in time, she will interrogate me about the girl's name, school, hair colour and distinguishing birthmarks. Rather than to tell her my intentions, I want to fool her into asking Demoiselle out for me without her knowing. This will be something I'll have to think about for the next few days. Also, I have to plan all the details, such as what to say, where we will meet, where to go and develop alternate plans B, C, D to M.

Thursday, April 28: Even if I was supposed to be getting my expensive and valued education, I worked out a date plan during class. What I could do is make Mum believe I've been assigned to be a supervising director for a play. The play would include:

- one amorous male dater
- one female datee
- one dog who drank too much water
- three scared fire hydrants
- A herd of singing yaks.

I could tell Mum that, being a director, I need to call the members of the cast to test them on their lines. I'll give Mum a list of questions from an official-looking script to read to Demoiselle, which will include the big question: "Will you go out with me this Saturday?" To make this look real, Mum will have to call at least five other people willing to play along. Oh boy—I'm starting to see the enormity of my task ahead. I'll have to write a short but plausible play, fabricate six characters, find five willing confederates, make five separate scripts for each person and have a mother who will not suspect a thing.

Another problem is this. How to anticipate a response to every possible reply Demoiselle could give, including "Yes, I'd love to go out with you" (which I hope she says) and "No, I have to take my cat's temperature that night." (In which case I'll proceed to disembowel myself). While Mr. Fry was explaining the evolutionary progress of the short-tailed vole using a tree diagram, I hit upon another great idea. I quietly thanked the education system for helping me. I'll map a "Yes/No" tree chart to anticipate Demoiselle's every possible response! I could draw it all on a giant poster-board, filled with ruler-straight lines, small explanatory diagrams and arrows pointing all over the place. A scientific approach would be the way to go.

Friday, April 29: The first problem to solve is picking the best night to call Demoiselle for a date. After dinner, I marched to the library to research upon courtship rituals. I found an obscure 1973 Nyasaland scientific journal called *TPMFCAOMOSYMWCLSOS* ("*The Process of Making the First Call to Ask Out a Member of the Opposite Sex You Met While Collecting Lost Socks Off the Street*"). In volume XIX, issue 6, I found a 38-page scholarly journal article that analyzed the best day to call a girl for a date. I struggled through the jungle of circular circumlocutions, hacked past entangled, twisted sentences replete with vague 16th century words, fought with wily and deceptive Möbius strip-like paragraphs, artfully dodged complex circuit board diagrams and swung over eleven pages of references in tiny print. In the end, I, weary and worn, triumphed against the dense tropical world of academia and learned one thing: Wednesday is the best day to ask for a date on Saturday night. Tuesday is too early and Thursday is too late as it wouldn't give her enough time to set a hair appointment. A Friday night call would make her think I ran out of people to call and phoned her after my overtures to Mrs. Coho's dog were rejected.

To my great disappointment, the Montreal Canadiens was eliminated in the first round of the Stanley Cup playoffs. As hockey is our religion, the proprietors of golf courses would be the only people happy with this.

Saturday, April 30: I worked out my plan "Demoiselle" all afternoon. It's starting to shape up. I told Mrs. Tautog that the script was a speech I have to do on Monday and we practised the "c" and "s" sounds in various words.

Mum and Dad spent the whole afternoon at a paper-littered dining room table filling out the federal and provincial tax forms. It's due today by midnight. I tried to tell them the merits of doing important tasks ahead of time but they were too busy arguing about a deduction.

Glancing through the forms, I noticed that Mum gave me a "disabled" status.

"Mum, I'm not disabled. We have no ramps leading to the front door," I protested.

"You're hearin' impaired, you're disabled, that is that," said Mum curtly.

May

Sunday, May 1st: I went over to see Luderick this afternoon and he told me how his date with Alfonsino was a bust. He went to the shopping centre last week in his drag as a lark and saw Alfonsino on the bench and, as a joke, winked at him. "He strutted up to me, slicked his eyebrows and panted, 'Hey babe, wanna boogie with me this Saturday?' as if he was a gift to women!"

Luderick remembered him from his Canterbury days despite the lack of hair. "I played along to see how long it would take for him to discover my real identity. So anyway, I made him pick me up from the same mall where we met. He came in this rare 1964 Cadillac Fleetwood car and his mom was driving. His mom, man, she was straight outta of a 1960s movie: big beehive hairdo, cherry earrings and pink poodle dress. Alfonsino stepped out like a hotshot, slicked his head and swaggered over to me with his shirt unbuttoned down to here, " he pointed to his mid-section, "and his mom yelled, in this loud squeaky voice, 'Button up your shirt, Alfie, you're gonna catch a cold!' and he grimaced and did up, like, two buttons. He says to me, 'Hey baby, don't worry about her, she's my chauffeur.' He sat with me in the back. I almost passed out from the reek of his dime-store aftershave and his mom was ragging him all the way to the dance, telling him to behave, keep his hands to himself, stay away from hot lights, blah, blah, blah." His mother had to pick him up after his hair caught on fire, cutting their date early. "Too bad—he didn't even get a chance to feel me up! Seeing his expression when he feels my rolled-up socks in my bra would've been priceless!" We laughed.

On this warm spring day, we played a new game called hacky sack. "Bend over and pick up the damn bean bag" would've been a better name. Our foot skills were akin to a near-sighted ostrich with two left feet. After about an hour or so of bending over, we went in and talked over grilled cheese sandwiches. His mother was in her shrine, muttering prayers amongst hundreds of candles. I think someone should alert the fire department. We talked about his idea that since sneezes travel over 150 kilometres an hour, we should be getting speeding tickets. No real conspiracies this time. I didn't tell him about my plans to ask Demoiselle. I don't want to waste energy telling him about my plan and waste more telling him how it didn't work out.

When I was cycling home, I saw Jake walking out of Mr. Fry's house carrying a TV set and, slowing down, I spied a frightened Mr. Fry peering out from behind curtains from the second floor.

Monday, May 2: For the operation "Demoiselle" script, I wrote a short play realistic enough to fool Mum starring Demoiselle as the love interest. The zero-day is Wednesday, only two days away!

Aside from the fake script, I also finished my date flowchart. I think I've been spending too much time preparing for this call because it's causing my schoolwork to suffer. Mr. Poisson gave me 42% on yesterday's French quiz.

I bought a new WWII airplane magazine and immediately put the centre-fold of a Hawker Sea Fury next to the giant poster of a Hurricane Mk IIA above my bed. Dad was passing by and stopped by my door, "Ah, you're rewarding yourself for a job well done at school. What good grade did you get?"

"I got my French test results."

"Brilliant, Egg. Keep up the good work my lad!" said Dad as he knocked off his pipe's ashes.

Journal, I'm not lying here. All I said I got the test back, but not what grade I received.

Tuesday, May 3: I was writing my weekly essay for Mr. Coley's class in the living room when Mum tapped me on the shoulder. "Egg, I've a late job interview tomorra at 5:30, so yer father will hafta make supper."

Dang! I need her to make The Call tomorrow. I hope her interviewer is a former auctioneer with ADHD, shooting his questions in rapid-fire succession.

Since there'll be a long-winded explanation to my mother about the intricacies of my plan "Demoiselle," I rehearsed my ruse for an hour tonight, using my pillow in place of my mother.

I don't know if this is an ominous sign or what but my hearing aid molds are getting loose. They aren't fitting into my ears as snugly as they should be.

Wednesday, May 4: I flip-flopped last night about making The Call; all sorts of niggling doubts were running through my mind. Since it has been more than a month since the last time I saw her, what if Demoiselle doesn't remember me? How would she react to a mother calling her? Will Mum blow my cover? What if she says one of the most dreaded words for any man to hear: "No, I'm not interested," "I just want to be friends," or "We're out of beer." I dragged myself out of bed at 4:30 a.m. to take another look at my flow chart and made a few revisions to include a backup situation in case our house catches on fire.

After an excruciating slow day at school, evening finally came. The goal of my mission was to have Mum call Demoiselle at around 7:30 p.m. She needed to arrive at least a half-hour before to give me time to explain my flowchart. Dad and I ate leftover supper together. He told me about a cow that swallowed a farmer's watch that was found two years later, still giving the correct time because the cow's breathing acted as an automatic winder. I didn't listen to the entire story, which included details of how they removed the watch using a magnet, because I kept glancing at the clock and the front door.

When supper was finished at 6:30, I put the FM system microphone near the door and attached the boot to my hearing aid so I would be able to hear Mum's entry from my bedroom while I did my homework. I couldn't concentrate on my studies because my head kept involuntary snapping to the bedside clock. Seven o'clock came and went without Mum's telltale slam of the front door. I turned up the volume of the FM system. To distract myself from the burbling of my stomach and humming of my tight nerves, I counted the number of scratches on my desk. The zero hour of 7:30 passed by without so much of a turn of the door latch. Two hundred and thirty scratches. I felt as if someone was slowly wrenching my stomach out of my body. I upped the FM's volume a bit more.

By 7:50, my stomach was being put through a Cuisinart. As I was trying to prevent this imaginary Cuisinart from going into the "puree" mode, a loud "BANG!" sounded and my hearing aid practically jumped across the room. Mum was home! I ran downstairs so fast I left little comic book smoke puffs. I watched Mum take off her coat while she complained to sympathetic Dad about how much time the interview took. It turned out that the interviewer was a former snail breeder.

I let her rest a bit and at 8:05, I went ahead, step-by-step, to accomplish my plan. First, I made sure Dad had returned to his den. He had. He was sitting in his favourite chair holding up a thick book titled, "*The Photographic Guide of Distinctive Teeth Patterns Found on Pencils.*" Next, I quietly tiptoed towards Mum in the kitchen. In my mind's eye, it was the CFL Grey Cup final, we were down 25–27 with two seconds left on the clock and I the kicker walked on the football field to attempt a 35-yard field goal. I first asked her how she was feeling to ascertain that she didn't feel ill, nauseous, or dizzy. My team lined up with the snapper who was posed to shoot the ball to the holder. All players were antsy and shifting. Mum reassured me she was perfectly fine and the interview didn't tax her too much.

So far, so good. I began my rehearsed speech and produced the poster chart. The stadium crowd fell deathly silent and I begin running towards the ball. Two minutes into my explanation about bidirectional Gaussian vectors, she stopped me and said, "You wanna me to cawl a girl for a date, that right?" Back in the game in my mind, Lucy Van Pelt snatched away the ball. I stood and stared at my mother as my synapses in my brain were frantically searching for an appropriate answer. Thousands of voices in the stadium gasped in horror.

"Uh, uh," I stammered and the best plan my brain could come up with were thoughts of spontaneously combusting. When I realized there was no way out of this, I gulped hard and forced a feeble, "Yes." My leg swings through the empty air next to a smirking Lucy. My elaborate, 17-minute explanation, the carefully crafted and geometrically pleasing chart, my rehearsed gestures flew out with my body as I landed on my back on the muddy field with my right leg sticking up.

But wait—penalty flag! A too many men penalty against the defensive team and a ten-yard penalty and it's 3rd down repeated! She didn't react in her usual overbearing, motherly, "Oh, my baby is growing up" fashion. She simply asked for Demoiselle's number and dialed. The field goal unit lined up for another field goal attempt and Lucy was yanked off the field.

Demoiselle answered the phone and my wonderful mother explained I had lost my voice and proceeded to ask Demoiselle if she would enjoy eating at Fillichi's restaurant on Saturday evening with me. She didn't mention my hearing impairment, thank her kind heart. People can run away in droves if they hear the words, "hearing impaired," thinking it's a disease that will make their chin fall off on a Thursday. I took three steps back and ran towards the football.

Demoiselle said, "Yes"! Field goal! We win! I'm going on a date with Demoiselle this Saturday! Not only that, it's only three nights away! I couldn't believe my fortune. My whole life thus far had been geared to this moment. It was involved in every wishbone wish, every coin thrown in a fountain and every "first-star-I see-tonight" wish. I dreamed of hearing a girl say, "Yes" and not be the answer to my question, "Are you going to punch me in the nose?"

This is the plan: Demoiselle will meet me at the Dorval bus terminus at seven o'clock this Saturday and we will walk to the restaurant together. Mum advised me to not bring her flowers and a box of chocolates because it's too "corny" nowadays.

"You can lead a horse to water but ya cannot make him fix yer air conditioner," she wisely quoted. "She says sorry for not comin' to the dance, her grandfather is very sick and may die soon. Oh another thang—she loves the silly poem you sent her 'n wants to know which cartoon you got it from."

Thursday, May 5: All my teachers' words fell on my deaf ears because I was daydreaming about my impending date with Demoiselle. I imagined myself, a debonair troubadour with ample hair covering my hearing aids, romantically swooning my new love with lyrical poetry of moonlights, flowers and soft kisses. I imagined us as passionate lovers gliding through clear moonlit waters in a pillow-laden gondola. I dreamt of us french-kissing high up on the Eiffel Tower and sipping champagne by a summer's river with a picnic spread before us. I pictured her nuzzling in my chest and whispering sweet nothings in my ear and I reply by saying, "What?"

It's the day after tomorrow!

During lunchtime, I overheard Alfonsino boast about one of his many sexual escapades. He says women lust for him because "Wimmin love to rub my bald head."

I'm worried—the issue of sex has been brought to the foreground for the first time. All I know about sex is the physiology of the reproductive system from Mr. Fry's class and Luderick's magazines. Sex education in school has left me ill prepared. How do I know what to do? School has not taught me any useful skills as unhooking a bra, how foreplay is related to "Fore!" in golf, or even about strange five-pronged sexual toys. I should know all this by now—all RCAF pilots know everything from A to Z and know how to handle women crawling over them in smoky bars. The educational system has inadequately prepared me for real life!

I saw Molly again, this time across the street talking to the same guy I saw her with last week. They were standing close and her arms were on his shoulders as they smiled and talked. You know what? It didn't bother me one bit. Someday, Demoiselle will do the same with me. But man—was she ever sexy with those high heel black shoes and short skirt.

Something *is* ominously wrong with the molds of my hearing aids, especially the left one. They're starting to feel loose. Every time I smile or laugh, my hearing aid molds pop out enough to make a squealing feedback sound. Mum noticed it, "You're whistling, dear." I lower the volume enough to stop the whistling but it becomes too low for me to hear properly.

My first date of my life is the night after tomorrow!

Friday, May 6: I had trouble sleeping again last night. I was bothered by a new worry: What should Demoiselle and I talk about? Fearing great glacial periods of silence wedging a chasm between painful words of datees, I turned my desk light on at 2:30 a.m. and wrote a list of interesting conversation starters. Here's part of the list:

- If everything in the universe, including our bodily processes and our watches were to go twice as fast, would we notice it? What about twice as slow? Grow two times the size? Shrink two times smaller? What would the world look like?
- Why do we call it fresh air if it's billions of years old? How does air become stale?
- If Einstein proposed that there is a curvature in space, what is space curving away from? What is outside this "curvature"? Will the two points eventually meet? On the other hand, given that space is infinite, would this curvature go on forever, never meeting?

When I reviewed this list, I felt dissatisfied. Too cerebral? Too bland? Too science-fiction? These were interesting topics Dad and I have discussed in the past and they've worked well. But will they work on a first date?

We had public speaking class today and I was fully prepared for the first time in my academic life. I gave a presentation on "Teethovin," a man in 17th century who had musical teeth. Mr. Bonito was pleased with my investigative efforts and said it was consistent with the theme topic— "Unusual musical instruments." I scored 91%! Alfonsino did a speech about a doctor who fell asleep every time he pressed his pants and snored in perfect pitch. He got 56%.

Jake, on the other hand, did better, scored a 70% on his presentation on sounds produced by punching people of different ethnic backgrounds. He demonstrated this with five frightened "volunteers": Lebanese Alfonsino, Italian Todd, Quebecois Jean-Pierre, Russian Ivan and Japanese Mori. Sure enough, each said "Ow" in different tones and pitches.

For gym class, we played rugby in the rain and cold mud. Mr. Barracuda, wallowing in his miserable, dank-apartment-with-the-shades-pulled-down-and-moldy-leftover-macaroni-and-cheese life of his own, tried his best to instill his brand of misery in our lives. I was impervious to his feeble attempts and managed to remain somewhat optimistic about my date tomorrow night (Tomorrow! It's less than 24 hours away!).

My molds are still loose. I got incessant reminders from different people about my hearing aids. Mr. Fry stopped in middle of an explanation about lemurs, "Mr. Flounder, your hearing aids are whistling."

Headmaster Sculpin squinted and bellowed, "Egg Flounder, your hearing aids are whistling!"

Alfonsino: "Hey man, you're whistling—you'll scare off dem chicks in no time flat—take it from me."

Jake: "Egg you turd—you're whistling! I'll shove your hearing aids where the sun don't shine!"

Bus driver: "Pay the correct fare. You're whistling."

I was hoping it would a temporary condition, like Leif Garrett's fame, but they whistle every time I yawn, smile, or laugh. A few moments ago I tried putting melted wax on the molds but it wouldn't stick properly. Wads of toilet paper stuck between the mold and the ear made me look too dorky. Argh! The date is tomorrow! There is no time to go see the hearing aid specialist. My first date and I'm gonna sound like R2-D2!

It went from bad to worse: I asked Mum to cut my hair. Bad idea number 104; you don't want to know what the other 103 were. I resemble an offspring between Andy Warhol and a Troll doll! Worse of all, she snipped too much hair off my sides and my hearing aids are exposed for all to see. On the day before my first date, no less!

Mum says not to blame her. "I've been worried sick about findin' a job and not havin' enough money to pay de bills." This is the last time I ask for a haircut from a depressed ex-hairdresser who watched the Siberia weather channel all afternoon ("Today's forecast—cold and snow. Stay tuned for more snow warnings").

Saturday, May 7: I didn't sleep at all last night. I was both excited about seeing Demoiselle and nervous about the hearing aid problem and the anguished state of my Warhol-Troll hair. Ninety-nine percent of my life thus far has been spent with functioning hearing aids and okay-looking hair—why did both fail at the same time now?

Mum blabbed to Mrs. Tautog about my date tonight so our speech drills were more intense. She also gave me a number of communication tips: pick a table in a quiet well-lit corner of the restaurant away from the noisy kitchen, sit with the wall behind me, ask Demoiselle to write down words I don't understand, etc. Her worse piece of advice was, "Tell her about your hearing impairment." Can you believe this? Yeah, right. I may as well as give her a megaphone to whisper love poems in my ear if she doesn't pick up her feet and bolt first.

I tried to remain in a positive state of mind and prepared myself for the date for the better part of the day— showered, chose my clothing carefully and slapped on Dad's good cologne. I combed my hair as best as I could and tried pulling my hair to cover both hearing aids, but it was hopeless. I decided to wear one hearing aid and keep Demoiselle on my unaided side.

Ostensibly, Mum served chili for supper. I refused to eat it because I didn't want my hearing aids to not to be the only source of musical noises and ate a peanut butter and banana sandwich and a salad (separately).

Dad didn't suspect a thing.

Mindful of the 7:00 p.m. meeting time, I grabbed a book from Dad's bookcase to read while waiting, took the #202 bus to the Dorval terminus and arrived there at 6:25. Once off the bus, I sat down to read the book and groaned—it was one of Dad's boring tomes: *"Instructions for Using an Eraser: The philosophy, physics and psychology of erasing."*

I found it difficult to read because of my conscious awareness of three things:

1) Time was moving as slow as the sales of a kazoo and spoon music tapes at a 99-cent bin at the Bay.

2) The uncomfortable sensation of my eyeballs snapping back and forth across the page.

3) My heart was pounding in my chest and my hands were quivering, blurring the words on the pages.

After reading the same paragraph four times, I shoved the book in my jacket. It was 6:38. I vainly tried to think of other things, such as the TV repairman whose claim to fame was being the only person who can sneeze from each nostril. It was no use—I couldn't calm myself down. I reviewed my conversational topic crib sheet with sweaty palms while my stomach flip-flopped and my head pounded. When the minute hand of my watch dragged towards the zero hour, I stood and stared at the bus stop where Demoiselle was supposed to get off. Tick by tick, my watch finally showed seven o'clock. No bus.

Five anxious minutes later, the bus arrived and my heart did a speeded-up version of the cha-cha. Several people disembarked and I frantically looked around. No Demoiselle. I looked at each ex-passenger again to make sure. Still no Demoiselle. I waited in agony for another 20 minutes for the next bus to arrive. She wasn't on that bus either! It was 7:30 and I felt as if several small furry creatures not unlike hamsters were eating me. I was ready to give up on dating and volunteer for vasectomy experiments by first-year medical school trainees when I felt a tap on my shoulder. It was she! Her expression wasn't what I thought I would see—it was a look that can make even the bravest of men wet their pants.

"You were at the wrong bus stop!" She frowned.

She apparently had arrived on time at 7:00 p.m., but on the other end of the bus terminus. She got off the westbound bus while I was waiting for eastbound bus. When the misunderstanding was cleared up, we walked to the restaurant in silence interspersed by a few awkward words. Her fine, sweet voice clashed with my croaky voice worse than a plaid shirt with a saber-toothed jacket. I could see glaciers ominously moving across the valley.

When we arrived at the restaurant, the headwaiter looked at us and joked, "Smooching or non-smooching section?" She laughed but I had to hold back because I was afraid my hearing aid would whistle. The waiter led us to the worse table in the room: it was lit by a pathetic little candle, had the kitchen door on one side and a large amplifier on the other. She sat across from me and I kept my head turned off the side to keep her from seeing the hearing aid and we quickly ordered. When the waiter left, I excused myself to go to the washroom.

After doing my business, I reached in my pocket to pull out a breath mint and my conversational crib sheet fluttered into the toilet. Argh! Holding my nose, I leaned over and tried to read the writing before it became a wet blue blob. No use. I returned to the table and while waiting for the meal to arrive, we made uncomfortable small talk, something I was dearly hoping to avoid. I brought up the curvature in space topic and her response was, "I don't know, how can space be curved in the first place?" I fell silent. Giant glaciers rumbled through a deep forbidding valley.

"Is your voice better?" she asked.

"Not really," I feebly croaked, excusing my ineptitude at the art of conversing.

She said something about her grandfather, hospitals, exams and other babble, a blur of words to me. I put on my Academy acting award in bluffing act and this kept her going for a solid 15 minutes. She finished her story and the silent walls of glaciers loomed again between us. We took quiet interest in our cutlery, the pattern on the napkin and anything else, except each other. The whole time I desperately tried to remember the other topics I wanted to bring up and thought how I would've preferred to have my spleen pulled out of my nostril. I was overjoyed when the meal arrived because it was an opportunity for us to do something else with our mouths other than to talk with it. The ice age was over.

During our meal, a comedian came on stage and entertained us, his voice booming from the amplifier on my left. Apparently, a rock band was supposed to perform but they went back to New Brunswick after their leader developed a fear of tight trousers. The comedian's specialty was slapstick humour and this made it miserable for me. I had such a hard time suppressing my laughter; I must've been making facial expressions not unlike sucking a lemon.

"Egbert, what's wrong?" Demoiselle asked when she saw my twisted expression. I think I shouldn't have told her that my mom bought me underwear that was too tight.

After dessert, the bill came. Demoiselle insisted on paying her half despite my protests. This marked my first step towards maturity. When I was a child, I never understood the adults' irrational insistence of paying a bill themselves. Since they loved money so much, I thought they should always let the other person pay. We strolled back to the bus terminus and waited for her bus to arrive. After ten minutes of silence and awkward glances at each other, the bus rounded the corner. Demoiselle turned to me and said, "Give me a call, I want to go out again."

Huh? She still wants to go out with me despite shivering through the ice age with a guy who looked as if he was passing a watermelon though the comedy act? I was in shock but happily so, if this is possible. Right before she boarded, she bent over and kissed me on the cheek. She kissed me! Wow! If a simple kiss on the cheek could excite me this much, I don't know what I would do if we were to make love—I would explode with excitement! The bus slowly pulled away and I blissfully watched her faint outline as it receded into the distance. I was too full of "happy energy" to take the bus, so I trooped three miles back home, half-skipping and half-jogging under the clear full moon. My mind and body floated with a heightened sense of expansion filling the infinite reaches of space. I can die now, my soul peacefully drifting among ethereal stars scattered across the velvet black sky far above. With such shivering excitement, I don't think I'll be able to sleep tonight.

It was such a perfect night.

Sunday, May 8: As predicted, I could hardly sleep last night. I kept replaying the moment when she kissed me. I'm happy she didn't suspect my hearing impairment—I would rather she see me as Egg Flounder first before seeing me as "that hearing impaired guy." I didn't realize how much love would make me feel so good! I woke up with a song on my lips, ate breakfast with zest and appreciated the little joys in life, such as not picking a piece of bread with a hole in it.

Luderick came over to my house after his usual Church mass. "It's such a waste of my time!" he wailed. "Can't I just set up a dummy in my place like famous people do when they're absent at the Oscars?" Since it was raining, we stayed in and played table hockey. Over grilled cheese sandwiches my mom made us, we talked about subliminal advertising. Luderick claims that the word "sex" is imprinted subliminally on everything—placemats, record covers and even on our living room curtains. "Yeah, if that is true," I argued, "how come we are not getting any?"

After supper, my parents went to a commemorative plate collector's colloquium, Ilisha went to a volleyball practice and I was left alone for the rest of the night. I was doing my geography homework when the phone rang. Since love has been reducing my brain into that of vegetable matter, I answered it.

It was Demoiselle!

I distinctly heard her say, "May I speak to Egbert please?" I stood there, transfixed on the kitchen floor, my heart was holding a vigorous aerobics class with the rest of my internal organs. I did a quick impression of an answering machine: "Please leave a message after the beep" and hung up. Not a good idea. Also, I forgot to add the "Beep."

I noticed her voice sounded different from yesterday—for all I know, the phone could distort people's voices.

I'll get Mum to call her again on Wednesday to ask her out to a movie this coming Saturday.

Monday, May 9: I couldn't concentrate in school today because my brain matter was devoted to Demoiselle all day even during the biology test (a test I naturally didn't know about). No matter how many times I replay the date and the kiss, I don't get sick of it. But *Tabernac*—I'm sure she thinks I'm a humourless lemon-eating monk because I didn't laugh at the comedian. I did permit a few giggles but I had to hold them in because it would've made my hearing aid whistle like a bomb warning. Damn molds! I asked Mum to make me an appointment on Friday with the hearing aid specialist downtown.

Wednesday, May 11: While my bus was picking up several people this afternoon, I saw Jake carrying groceries with Mr. Fry's wife and his 13-year-old daughter, smiling as if he was an innocent boy scout. Yeah, a boy scout from middle-east guerrilla troops.

I got the biology test back with room temperature grade in Celsius: 21%. This love business is starting to have a negative effect. How could I feel good about the world and know where the spleen is at the same time?

Dad says I need to be more prepared for future assignments if I'm serious about going to college.

After dinner, when Dad retired to his den to read, "*Illustrated do-it-yourself book on home surgery.*", I snuck up on Mum and asked her to call Demoiselle. Given she wasn't too happy that she was passed over for a job today, I had to drag her away from the TV to do her part. Mum, despite her despondency, did a wonderful job. She lied again to Demoiselle for me, saying that I cannot talk because I came home from the dentist with half of my mouth still frozen. Mum asked her if she could see a movie with her son this Saturday. Demoiselle said yes! For the second straight time, a girl didn't tell me she will be too busy giving a suppository to her pit bull.

Demoiselle and I decided to meet each other at the Peel metro station downtown at 7:30 p.m.. Now that I've had my first dinner date, I'll soon experience the first joys of being in a dark, intimate theatre with a member of the opposite sex without the need to chitchat.

Thursday, May 12: In the Atwater metro I saw Jake at the exit corner stuffing several running shoes, Oxfords and ladies' black flats into his gym bag. I scooted by, paid the fare and jumped on the metro along with several other students and four nuns. They all were wearing only socks.

The day after tomorrow is the movie date! I have no idea what movie we're going to see. Demoiselle said we would decide when we meet. At this exact moment, I had a shocking revelation. What if she wants to talk about the movie after? How will I know what the movie is about if I won't understand a damn word the actors are saying? I thought going to a movie would be a brilliant idea since I wouldn't have to talk about my in-grown toenail.

I hope we don't see a movie with a lot of dialogue. If it has a lot of action with verbal exchanges consisting of Neanderthal grunts and anyone with at least two working brain cells would understand the plot, I'll do fine. However, I don't think Rambo-style movies would be a good first-date choice. Court dramas would be the absolute worst—too much lip flapping. Comedies would be acceptable as long as they use visual humour. Horror movies aren't bad, but if it requires a complex psychological explanation of why the killer was terrorizing people by dressing up as a Flamenco dancer, I don't want to see it. It's time to head to the library again to do some research.

Friday, May 13: On my way out of school today, I spied Jake trying to set the school shed on fire with a magnifying glass trained on a pile of dry leaves. I didn't have the heart to tell him that a flashlight wouldn't work.

I went to Mr. Halibut the hearing aid specialist to get new molds made. Not only he made the impressions of my ears to send to the mold manufacturers, he also put on a temporary rubber piece over my old molds to make them tighter. Until I get the new molds, I'll be able to smile and laugh without making that annoying whistle and causing so many scrunched up faces around me.

After supper, I went to the library to read scientific journals on acceptable types of movies for dates. I want a movie that will make her fall in love and yet be visual enough for me to understand the plot. I thought romantic movies would do the trick, but according to an article in "*The Journal of Dating: The Scientific Approach*", horror movies are "most conductive to stimulating attraction from the opposite sex." Apparently, the most effective movies are those that register at least a 8.1 out of ten on the Gruenstein Suspense Level Scale (GSLS) and contain between 5.7 and 7.3 acts defined as "eliciting an innate misdoubt response within wide-band parameters that embodies a significant etiology resulting in a post-sentient event that encompasses or imperils a cessation of indispensable utilities."

In other words, murders.

Now I've a better idea of what kind of movie to see, I've been thinking: since Demoiselle is the first girl I've gone out with and we're going out on a second date (this is what they probably mean by "second base"), I wonder how will I give my first kiss. Not a peck on the cheek—a lip kiss. How do I kiss a girl on the lips? How much pressure should I put on them? How long? Will our noses get in the way? No journal articles covered this vexing topic, except for one that touched upon the Eskimo custom of rubbing noses. I don't think she would appreciate it if I grabbed her ears and wiped her nose on my schnoz. I think I'll be flip-flopping again tonight.

Saturday, May 14: I didn't fall asleep until 4:23 am, but once I did, I slept in as much as possible so most of the day would be used up and thus lessen the stress of waiting for the time to meet my love. The less stress my young body experiences, the longer I'll live and the more time I'll spend with her. Before rising from my bed, I thought more about the kissing situation for another ten minutes before Mum caught me kissing my pillow.

"I'm practicing mouth-to-mouth resuscitation for a gym test," my excuse went.

All day I did my homework so I wouldn't feel guilty about going out tonight. I even cooperated with Mrs. Tautog. I should've not told her that I have a hot date at the movies tonight. She looked at me with raised eyebrows, "You know you have difficulty understanding what they say in movies. Wouldn't this be your opportunity to tell her about your handicap so she can explain the movie's plot afterwards?"

I almost blurted out, "Handicap? How can I tell her? I don't play golf." I decided to keep my mouth shut.

Anyway, at 4:00 p.m., I showered, got dressed and again took off one hearing aid. I ate an early supper at 5:30. After Mum bade me good luck, I took the bus downtown and arrived at the Peel metro subway at 7:10. At 7:25, five minutes before I was to meet my new beloved, I spied, of all people, Molly riding up the escalator. Her eyes locked on my mine and I froze.

"Hi Eggie!" she shouted as she strutted towards me in her high heels. Her nipples were poking out of her tight blouse. Damn! The last person I wanted Demoiselle to see me with!

"Whom are you waiting for?" she said coyly.

I stared at her blankly and a horrible, yet unrelated thought dawned upon me: Demoiselle told me to meet her at an exit, but it was then I remembered that the metro has four exits. Which one was it?

"See you later, I've to go!" I bolted, leaving a gorgeous girl looking puzzled. I ran outside, crossed the street and went to exit #2. I waited there for five minutes in panic and anxiety. I didn't see her. What would a real RCAF pilot do in this situation? I had a personal debate whether to stay another five minutes or to continue my search at exit #3 and my brain cells made a democratic vote by the show of hands. "Continue search" won over "stay" by a close margin, although a few cheated by raising two axons. I went back out, dodged speeding cars and ran for exit #3. When I approached the door, blood was coursing through my body and my heart was fighting out of my skinny chest. I felt Demoiselle's presence close by. I pushed through the revolving doors and I hunted around, my head whipping this way and that. No Demoiselle. My sinking heart was going "Glub glub glub" as it sank below the sea of despair. Where could she be? I waited another five minutes and decided to return to exit #1 instead of trying for exit #4. At this point, 32 minutes had already passed. I sprinted back outside, again played "Frogger" with onrushing cars to arrive, in one piece, at exit #1. I found Demoiselle looking out the window and Molly was gone—whew. With my heart playing the "Inna

Gadda Da Vida" drum solo, I approached her.

"Egbert!" she exclaimed, "Where the hell did you go? As soon I came in here, I saw you running out! I yelled 'Egg, Egg!' but you ran across the road!" She arrived at the exact moment when I bolted to check exit #2. Tabernac! Only if I had waited another 15 seconds!

"I called your name five times while you were running off!"

I gulped. On the other hand, she would've seen me with Molly.

We walked to the theatre in silence and I kept an eye out for Molly, coiled and ready for an evasive maneuver should I spot her. We found the theatre three blocks away and quickly decided on a movie to see. I wanted to see "Jaws 3-D" but Demoiselle wanted to see "Lawyers: A 3-Hour Court Drama With lots of Talking" starring Rob Lowe and Marlon Brando, reprising his mumbling role from "The Godfather." She convinced me to see her movie by using her wily charm and beauty. All she said was, "Please" in a pitiful and mournful voice that would've made anyone fork over large amounts of cash to ensure the survival of city pigeons. I paid for the both of us. We were 15 minutes late and the theatre was dark and crowded. After several minutes of fumbling around, I managed to find the last two empty seats next to each other in the back corner. I called after her but she didn't turn around and I lost the chance when two women plopped there. So, in my first movie date, my first chance to make a move on Demoiselle, we sat separately. I sat next to a red-haired cow of a woman whose sole fixation was her washing-machine-sized popcorn container, pieces dribbling off my lap. A bored young kid behind me kicked at my seat for the entire movie, my seat jiggling enough to rattle my teeth, but kept me from nodding off. Worse of all, not one scene featuring an airplane.

After the movie (I was never so happy to see the credits), Demoiselle and I met outside the theatre. We didn't have much to say about the movie because we missed a crucial crime scene in the beginning and thus the rest of the movie was incomprehensible. Aside from this, she thought it was an "Ok movie but Rob Lowe is such a hunk!" THAT was the only reason why she wanted to see the movie in the first place! From my point of view, the movie was a classic snooze—it could've been made in Quechuan for all I care. I didn't understand as much as two or three words, let alone the damn plot. There wasn't a single nudity scene to keep my eyes propped open. The only bare breasts I saw were at a dinner table next to the cranberry sauce. I think there should be a law that all big-screen movies have subtitles for us hearing impaired folks.

It was about eleven o'clock when the movie finished and we decided to go home. As we walked back to the Peel metro station, something wonderful happened—she held my hand! I never realized that holding hands would be such a wonderful feeling. I wish we were able to sit next to each other in the theatre because we would have held hands throughout the tedious court drama. We even talked a bit. She goes to Queen's college, has two younger brothers and is planning to be a coroner, a scientist who examines dead bodies to find out the cause of death. Her father is a coroner himself and when she was a child, he would teach her the finer points of autopsies, including putting tags on the corpses' toes without tickling them. With this early education, she became enamored with the profession. Coroners are in great demand and she would do a lot to help detectives solve murders and mysterious deaths. I didn't understand most of what she said because she was talking into my unaided ear, but I was able to lip-read enough to get the gist. I told her I prefer to die in my sleep like my grandfather did, not screaming in terror like the passengers in his car.

While waiting for her metro train which was going the opposite way from mine, I became aware that the date was soon over, that we would be separating and a goodnight kiss was in order. She was still holding my hand and her warm body was standing close to mine.

Her words passed from one ear and out the other as I dreamingly stared at her lips. Several thoughts ran through my mind over the drone of her voice: should I make lip-to-lip contact on a second date? How long should I do it? What if I missed and kissed her nostril? Without warning, her train arrived. She glanced at it, turned to me and piped up, "OK, bye Egg, call me soon," and gave me a quick kiss on my cheek. Before I could react with my own lips, she had already embarked. She gave a little wave as the doors slid shut and the metro roared away.

Argh! I lost my chance to kiss her! Again! Not that I was unhappy with the peck on the cheek, but I wanted to express my love to her with our unusual human tendency of lip mashing. All the way home, I kicked myself for over-analyzing the approach to a simple lip kiss and missing my chance. Next time, I'll plan my approach an hour before and not in the last seconds.

Sunday, May 15: I woke up this morning and stayed in bed, evaluating last night's date. I couldn't say if it was a bad, fair, good, or excellent date because I've had only one other date in my lifetime to compare it with. A large chunk of my time at the movie was spent looking at the armrest, trying to figure out how I could knock away the cow-woman's bucket of popcorn. I've forgotten how much I hate those kinds of armrests.

First, you have "elbow wars" over the monopoly of the single armrest to be shared with the person next to you.

Secondly, we males cannot make those decent, subtle moves on our dates. If Demoiselle had sat next to me, I would've preferred to hold her hand instead of swinging my ape arms around her shoulders. I noticed if I ever wanted to hold a girl's hand, the damn armrest would be in the way. It's always too thick to do it under or over it. It should be one of those swing-back types seen on planes: you flip it up to hold the girl's hand comfortably.

It gave me an idea. I took a fresh sheet of paper and wrote my next essay for English literature—a fictional history of how movie theatre armrests came to be.

I suspect the Church in the prudish 1950s controlled the design of movie theatre armrest. When teenagers went on dates in alarming frequencies, the "testosterone-driven behaviours of wild male teenagers towards innocent, devout teenage choir girls" worried the Church. To them, the teenage male was an uncontrollable jiggling mass of zits, testosterone and leather so sexually frustrated that his hair was capable of producing enough grease to power a small bus. They had a notion that teen males, if without a girl in a dark movie theatre to satisfy their urges, will hump anything, including their grandmother's Victorian chair.

To control the raging male passion, the Church ordered the theatres to install large, stiff armrests to separate the participants. The first armrests were two feet high, three feet wide and four inches thick. Big burly ushers patrolled the aisles with flashlights so bright it left people with sunburns. Side note: It used to be a male badge of honour to have a deeply sun burnt face the next day to show that the usher had discovered the guy and his date on more than one occasion. It wasn't until after a few stud-wannabes intentionally burnt their faces with a sunlamp did this male badge of honour have less effect.

As society became more liberal, the size of the barrier gradually shrank, being replaced with smaller and smaller armrests. However, we still have armrests interfering with the participants' ease in holding hands and making other sorts of moves commonly frowned upon by blue-haired Bridge-club ladies. With the progression of sexual liberalism, I predict they will disappear and become replaced by small sofas for couples. The theatre could someday be divided into two sections—sofas and the usual single chairs with armrests. The usher would say to you, "couples, or non-couples?" Beds could replace the small sofas and the theatres would have baby-delivering rooms next to the snack bars, complete with doctor-ushers. Thus, you will need to have a medical degree to be an usher. And next to the baby-delivering room, there would be a mini-chapel, so religious people could get married before the procreating during a geriatric Stallone feature, *Rambo 12: Wrinkled, Constipated and Toothless.*

I read an interesting bit of news in this morning's paper. It concerned a private security officer with a certification and training in performing physically demanding tasks such as breaking through doors and subduing violent suspects. At his workplace, he was granted a handicapped parking permit because of a sinus problem. If he can get such a break, I should be given half-price tickets to movies because I can only understand half of the plot.

I wanted to lay to rest my worry that my future-wife-to-be Demoiselle won't do vivisections on me while I'm asleep, I asked Dad if a desire to be a coroner represents evidence of a twisted mind.

"Absolutely not, Egbert. It can be a healthy interest. Society has become too bloody neurotic and fearful over the concept of death. We should have a healthy attitude towards it and not worry whether people will bring cheap casseroles to your funeral."

He also reminded me Mum's birthday is on Wednesday.

When Mum went out with Mora, the phone rang and Dad answered it. Ilisha jumped off the sofa and yelled, "It's for me!" She stopped at her tracks when he handed me the phone, "It's for you—it's a girl."

I went into a momentary shock when I realized that:

A) The girl is Demoiselle

B) Dad is going to stand there and translate for me

C) If A is correct, Demoiselle is going to find out I'm hearing impaired, given the evidence of B.

Kicking myself for not having a backup plan, I took the phone with great dread and made a feeble "Hello?" I stood before Ilisha's open-mouth stare and Dad's steely gaze. Sure enough, it was she and I had a blender of happiness and uneasiness.

Thinking fast, I blurted in a different voice, "Hi Mrs. Demoiselle, I promise to bring the paint set for art class on Wednesday.

I heard Demoiselle pause and say something similar to, "Oh, O.K., talk to you soon," and we hung up.

Ilisha and Dad never looked so puzzled. "But you don't have a paint set," Dad remarked. At least they still don't know about my new love. Not yet.

I think this call is a good thing, according to one article in "*Journal of North American Mating Behaviours of Adolescent Humans with Pimples.*" The researchers labelled it as the "post-date call," when "A datee establishes a form of a next-day communication channel with the participant from a prior nocturnal ritualistic mating protocol as a method of demonstrating actions known as 'selection of propagation enhancement.'"

Monday, May 16: Headmaster Sculpin personally visited each classroom to announce that an important group of nuns and investors will be coming to our school.

"I can't tell you how important that *all* of you", he paused, his beady eyes scanning our faces. "To be on your best behaviour to reflect the high quality of our programs." Apparently, the nuns are from Italy and they were robbed last week, their shoes taken by a large unidentified boy. They were not too pleased.

After school, I went shopping for Mum's birthday present. Not an easy task. I usually get her a box of chocolates because it always meant she would have to share. I couldn't get chocolates this time because Dad had already bought her a giant box. After a few hours of searching, I went to a perfume counter attended by a blond woman in a low-cut blouse and an eye-popping cleavage. Noticing she has to bend over to get a bottle from under the counter, I became indecisive, and after showing me seven different perfumes, I settled on a small bottle of "Eau de Toilette" called Fleur de Rocaille. I hope it's perfume—I didn't notice the name until I got home. If I wanted to buy a toilet product, I would've bought her Ty-D-Bowl.

On my bed, I found a new paint set. "It's for your art class, Egg," Mum said. Oh yeah, that. And, I don't even take art.

Tuesday, May 17: I got back my essay on movie theatre armrests with 90% mark; Mr. Coley wrote on the margin, "Funny and inventive!"

Mr. Fry took our class to a short field trip in the woods near the school to teach us about different plants and trees on this nice spring day. Jake was his usual violent self, stomping on flowers, pulling wings off flies and throwing rocks at the poor squirrels. The last act of delinquency pushed Mr. Fry over the edge. His face became beet red, his shoulders shook and he reamed him in front of 23 impressed boys. This was a scene to be seen—a short red-faced man yelling at a giant stomach. For the first time, the bully didn't fight or talk back. We all stood transfixed among the silent trees, staring at spectacle, our eyes as big as coffee saucers. We all were wondering which process of selection would win: the big-eats-small concept or the higher-man-on-the-ladder-of-success-and-authority concept. I'm happy to announce that the latter won. Mr. Fry sent Jake to the principal's office to get his detention slip. Jake hung his head and trudged off with big slow feet. The brave teacher turned his attention to us and calmly conducted the rest of the field trip to a rather subdued group.

I called Demoiselle tonight. Since I ran out of excuses for not talking directly to her (you can only go to the dentist so many times), I put the phone on the table for Mum to hear and did all the talking this time. She listened in and mouthed and gestured everything she said. When I asked her if she wanted to go out this Saturday, she said, "Sorry, my family is going to Guelph."

"Sounds like fun, I hope you get a hole-in-one." She laughed. I frowned and Mum quickly wrote, "Not golf—Guelph." Looked the same on the lips.

"I promise to see you at the dance next Saturday. I'm looking forward to being with you again," Demoiselle said and Mum mouthed. Even though I was melting like a chocolate bar in a hot glove compartment, I was cool and told her, "I'll call you again next week. Enjoy yourself this weekend."

Wow! A girl is honestly interested in me! I never thought this was possible. I had a warm and jubilant feeling all over. Flying a F-86F Sabre would never make me feel this good.

It was great having Mum interpret for me. I wish I could use her for school, she could interpret what the teachers say when they turn around and talk to the blackboard and relay student's questions, both I miss by long shots.

Wednesday, May 18: After the reaming incident in the woods yesterday, Jake was noticeably quiet in Mr. Fry's class. He sat stock-still, arms folded and glared at our teacher. He didn't make his usual rude cow-in-heat noises, clean his Remington deer rifle, or carve his name on Alfonsino's arm. I cherish the new sense of silence and flow in class.

It was Mum's birthday today. She was thrilled with Dad's present, a fancy box of truffles from Heyez Chocolatier. We all ate half of the box in five minutes flat. After she received my present, the so-called "Eau de toilette," she said, "I thank you very much from the bottom of my heart, Egg," and gave me one her sloppy motherly kisses. At least she didn't say it would make her toilet bowl smell good.

Thursday, May 19: I'm ashamed to write that now a whole group of new people are on my list of those who have seen my penis aside from my parents, my doctor and me. Firstly, I should've not drunk the huge bottle of cola for breakfast. Secondly, no matter what they say, you don't do nature's business in nature. While in Latin class this morning, my bladder was ready to burst so I excused myself. I walked into the washroom to see the big back of Jake bending over the sink and washing blood off his hands. This incident goes into the death prevention category of "I didn't see this" and I bolted out before his squinty eyes could spy his next corpse-to-be.

I went out the door next to the cafeteria, crawled through the line of bushes along the stone walls and, finding a perfect spot, I stood up to release the remains of two litres of soft drink into the lilacs. As I was letting out a long, satisfying, "Ahhhhhhh," I heard a loud knock from the window next to me. Mrs. Anchovy! Damn! I pissed in front of her office! I twisted around, tried to pull up my zipper but it was stuck and my feet got entangled in the branches. I fell backwards into the open, my dick sticking out. The Italian nuns! Headmaster Sculpin!

Headmaster Sculpin grabbed me by my collar and leap-frogged me inside, my male member flopping here and there, while he shouted in my ear. I was shut in a small, empty windowless room in the school's basement alone until Mum arrived with a scowling headmaster. She gasped, "Oh Egg, what were you doin' exposin' yerself to all dose nice people?"

Headmaster Sculpin, hands firmly on lapels, stood behind her. "This is conduct unbecoming of a Canterbury student. We have an important reputation to uphold to the academic community. If a young man like you cannot control his sexual urges..." and rest were dripping with sarcasm and distain not worth repeating. He said "sexual" in the same manner as "first degree murder" and suspended me for three days. Mum drove me home in silence. Dad wasn't pleased either. Ilisha only grinned, "So they saw how small your dinky is, eh?"

Friday, May 20: First day of suspension. Stayed in my bedroom all day long among my airplane posters and models, a RCAF POW with TV privileges.

Mum came back from a job interview and got a job! It's at a fruit packing plant in Laval where she will start on Monday as a quality control inspector. It sounds high-end and fancy.

The best news of the day: there will be an airplane show on Sunday. The *Montreal Star* reported that the planes will be flying in from different parts of Canada and U.S. tomorrow morning and will land on the private runway next to the Dorval Airport in preparation for the show the next day.

Saturday, May 21: I woke up at 5 a.m. and cycled to the airport. In my backpack, I carried Dad's pair of binoculars, lunch (two chocolate bars), a note pad for recording sightings and a small folding stool. Upon arriving, it began to drizzle. Damn—I forgot my raincoat. I put my hearing aid in my backpack and by the time the first plane flew overhead after an hour of sitting, it was raining at a fast clip. The two other plane-watchers jumped into their truck and rumbled away, leaving me alone in the field. When the Benbrook Lightning roared past, it poured buckets. I shivered on the damp stool, my notepad became soggy and water dripped down my back. No matter—I kept the binoculars trained to the distant skies.

Five hours and 12 planes later, buckets of rain poured upon the cold muddy ground and pooled around my shoes, I ate the remaining wet chocolate bar, folded up the stool and cycled home under dark skies. It was a great day! I saw seven live vintage planes flying over me, only to be seen once in my lifetime. According to my smudgy notebook, I witnessed the flights of the Hurricane Mk IIA, Luftwaffe Eagle, B-25, Halifax Bomber, De Havilland Mosquito, Salford Lancaster, CF-18 Hornet and five Canadian Forces Snowbird planes. As I stared at their slow descent upon the runway, dreams of flying these majestic machines filled my mind. I was in bliss except when Mum berated me for missing liver-lips Mrs. Tautog's lessons.

It was strange staying at home on this Saturday night. For the last two wonderful Saturdays, I had my heartstrings plucked by Demoiselle, even though they are badly in need of tuning.

The dance is next week! Seven more nights from now, I'll be holding Demoiselle's lovely body close to mine, our hearts beating as one.

Sunday, May 22: This sunny morning Dad and I went to the air show near the airport where I saw my dream planes all over again. Even though we saw the planes up close, the experience wasn't as good as yesterday. Watching them yesterday was a more personal experience, a private bliss having the entire sky above me, only me and the planes. We gaped at the Canadian Forces Snowbird air stunts and Dad asked me all sorts of good questions about how they did the stunts. I happily explained everything to him, touching on the Kutta-Joukowski theorem and the manipulation of the ailerons with details on angles of yaw axis.

I visited Luderick later in the afternoon. Since it was a nice day, we went to the park to throw the baseball around. On the way there, we spied Jake and Mr. Fry's 13-year-old daughter in the far corner of the park—they were kissing! Luderick and I hid in the bushes until they left. He still gets nightmares of Jake throwing him in front of a snowplow. We sprinted to the far opposite corner of the field and played catch for short time.

Back at his place, Luderick talked about how toilet paper is specially designed to never tear in a straight and neat line despite its abundant perforations. A tiny triangular piece from the next strip always appears, ruining the aesthetic looks of a straight-torn sheet. Luderick eagerly demonstrated with this repeatedly with a roll in his bathroom.

"This is done on purpose to make us consume more toilet paper," he whispered.

"Luderick," I looked him in the eye, "people don't care if it's perfectly torn, it's only for wiping, it's not art. They wouldn't keep on tearing strips of toilet paper until it's aesthetically pleasing." He paused and looked up to the ceiling. I think he saw my point.

Monday May 23: Second day of suspension. Before Mum went to work at the fruit packing plant, she woke me up at 7am, mouthing in my squinty eyes, "Get up 'n wash the dishes and mop th' floors, and don't sit around and do nothin' again!" Like a good boy, I went back to sleep. I lolled about and thought about Demoiselle and the impending dance all day. In a soft-focus daydream scene, I, a RCAF pilot in a sharp military tuxedo and shiny black shoes, was with Demoiselle in a glittery sequined dress. We gracefully danced to twinkling music from Oscar Peterson under a clear starry night. As the song slows, I pulled her closer and our eyes met. We softly stared into each other's eyes as our bodies swayed with the beat of the gentle music. As the song faded to an end, our lips drew closer together and they met with a surge of warm electricity. A great crescendo rose from the band as we kissed passionately under millions of sparkling stars above.

Back to reality, Mum finished her first day at work. She says it's the most boring job she's ever had. As a quality control inspector, all she has to do is to watch oranges travel down a conveyer belt and pick out the bruised ones.

"Am I gonna to watch thousands of oranges zippin' by for the rest of mah life?" she wailed to Dad. I think I should put more effort in my schoolwork from now on. At least she didn't notice the unwashed dishes and dirty floor.

Tuesday, May 24: Third day of suspension. Dad told me that my new molds are ready to be picked up from Mr. Halibut's office. The appointment is on Friday. I'm relieved they're ready because soon I no longer have to deal with people saying, "You're whistling" and the old molds have become yellowed and inflexible, like the Tory party.

It's 11:30 p.m. as of this writing and I remembered now that I have to give a speech for public speaking class tomorrow. I don't know what topic we were supposed to talk about but I'll think of something in the morning on the way to school.

Wednesday, May 25: Back to school after the POW experience. While on the bouncing bus, I was watching middle-aged men on their way to work when I hit upon a topic for my five-minute speech. I quickly jotted it down and memorized it. My speech was about a phobic forest ranger who paid for a tattoo of a spider on his bald head to scare the flies away. Mr. Bonito sighed from the back of the class, his walrus mustache puffing out, "Your speech was too short, it was terrible and it didn't touch on this month's topic, 'foreign income tax systems.' Your grade is 48%."

Damn! I've one more speech to go and I must do well on it. If I don't, I'll fail the course and won't graduate. A horrible image came to me: I'm an older man standing next to my even older mother in a large factory and we are staring at hundreds of oranges as they zip by on a conveyer belt.

My classmates heard about my indecent exposure incident. At lunchtime, I found a hotdog with two grapes at each side at my place on the cafeteria table when I returned from buying a soft drink. While I was looking at it quizzically, the other guys at my table sniggered. "Hey Egg," Peter Guppy spoke up, "your hot dog is showing!"

I saw Molly sitting alone at my bus stop after school and not wanting my hot feelings for her to conflict with those for Demoiselle, I hid around the corner until the bus picked her up with a bunch of other people. I got on last and sat in front far from her.

Since today is Wednesday, it was time I gave Demoiselle a pre-dance call. Mum was by my side to translate and I dialed her number. For the first time, a man answered the phone. Her father! My future father-in-law! With gusto, I blurted, "Hello, sir, this is Egg Flounder."

"Who?" Mum mouthed.

"Egg Flounder."

"Are you talking about some kind of fish?"

"No, sir, that's my name. I'm sure your daughter has told you all about me."

"I never heard of you. Do you have nasal congestion?"

"No, sir. This is the way I speak," I answered, mildly annoyed.

"Are you the guy who was supposed to fix the furnace?"

"Uh, no, sir," I gulped.

"Is this Lamprey Snow joking me?"

"No, sir. Never mind. Good night."

And that was it. I never spoke to her. Who is Lamprey Snow and why do I have a bad feeling about this? Mum said the father sounded rude and annoyed as if I was interrupting something.

Thursday, May 26: Guess what? Jake was expelled! Yup, one month away from his high school graduation and he gets the boot. What's more, guess who did the honours? Mr. Fry! Mr. Fry was showing us a film about fish behaviour and Jake was making his usual rude bodily noises and doing fish voiceovers. It was something we all expected from him but, after one especially loud imitation of hippopotamus belch, the class lights went up.

We all turned to see one pissed-off teacher standing next to the light switch, his teeth clenching, his jaw muscles twitching and the vein on his neck throbbing. He slowly walked up to the big guy in the back of the class, his furious eyes drilling into him. For the first time in history, Jake looked scared. Mr. Fry spewed forth a torrent of angry words and chewed him out in front of the class with much finger jabbing. Jake tried to size himself up over the diminutive teacher in feeble attempt to re-gain his power, but deflated at the exact words every schoolboy fears: "Come to the office with me." Being sent to the office is nothing compared to going the office with the teacher.

They left together and were gone for a good 25 minutes as my classmates jabbered excitedly among themselves. Mr. Fry forgot to turn off the FM system microphone and I sat still and listened in but, without lips to read, he might as well have been ordering lunch. All I heard was a stream of serious and angry voices and then it cut dead. This was when Mr. Fry remembered to turn the microphone off.

Several minutes went by and the door swung open and the class went quiet in a split-second. Mr. Fry motioned Jake to the back of the class and commanded, "Clean out your desk."

Jake's shoulders' were slumped and he had a long look on his face. I saw something eerily different about him; I couldn't put my finger on it. He was no longer the Jake we once knew, as if someone else is wearing his skin, shades of *One Who Flew Over the Cuckoo's Nest*. He plodded to the back of his class and a little part of me, just a teeny part, felt sorry for the big guy.

"Class, I have an announcement," Mr. Fry spoke up to a hushed crowd. "Jake has been expelled." A wave of stunned shock and awe swept over the class. He had the guts to kick him out of school! We all stared at Jake as he opened his desk to collect his brass knuckles, hunting knives and bullet casings. All 25 pairs of eyes followed him as he shuffled out of the class. As he passed my desk, I detected a tear welling up his eyes. I think he was sad to leave behind his mounted deer head on the wall.

When I arrived home, I found Mum watching *"Computer Chess-by-mail Championships"* on TV in the darkness of the basement. A vacant look was frozen on her face as the lights flickered over her tired eyes.

In the kitchen, Dad took me aside and advised, "Avoid your mother for now. She got sacked this morning." Sacked? How could she get laid off from such a simple job as inspecting oranges?

When I went to my room, I found a large package from Royal Aviation College on my bed. Quickly opening it with trembling fingers, I read the cover letter with my heart pounding. I've been accepted! Not accepted accepted—I've been short-listed and have one last task to do. The letter gave a date and time of my entrance interview. Interview? Reading further, I learned it's an evaluation process where my "aptitude, abilities, suitability for the program will be assessed by a panel of five judges."

"Yikes!" I screamed to myself and my hair did a handstand. The interview is scheduled Monday, June 27 at 14:00. Another line read, "Your acceptance into Royal Aviation College will be revoked if an update of the applicant's final secondary school grades prove unsatisfactory." Why in every mental scene of lush rolling hillsides, fields of sweet-smelling flowers and puffy white clouds swimming across the deep blue skies, there is a belching grey smokestack in the background? I told my parents the news.

"That's wonderful," she mumbled without taking her eyes off the screen.

Dad patted my back, "Despite your hearing impairment, you're becoming a successful young man." I don't know about the "man" part—I don't even have stubble yet and my arms are still as thin as fishing poles.

No matter—the dance is the night after tomorrow! I can't wait to see Demoiselle again!

Friday, May 27: As I was going towards my locker this morning, I saw a group of classmates hanging around, sniggering and smiling. I opened my locker and a roar of laughter exploded behind me—in my locker door was a picture of an old nude nun with boobs hanging to her knees.

Peter slapped my back, "Hey, is this your new girlfriend?" More laughter rang the air as my face reddened. When everyone shuffled off to class, I took the picture off, wrote something evil in the corner and put in an envelope. I know exactly where to put it.

Everyone at school has been talking about Jake's expulsion. Many of his former victims expressed relief, including me. There was talk of forming a "Former Victims of Jake" therapy group but the auditorium wasn't available.

How Mr. Fry managed to screw up enough courage to do this? Apparently, he took a self-help night course exclusively for men called, "Don't be a doormat, be tough." Its purpose is to help wimpy men gain more confidence and more control over their lives. To be eligible for this course, participants must have at least two of the following tendencies:

- Cannot say "No" to any request, even to people asking to borrow your clean underwear.
- Have difficulty speaking for yourself, even when someone is standing on your foot.
- Quietly pays parking tickets on time even if you were parked in your own driveway.
- Is bothered daily by large, hairy-backed, Neanderthal men with a vocabulary range of 54 words.

With each succeeding week, Mr. Fry became increasingly confident of himself and his ability to be a figure of authority to boys not old enough to know the meaning of the word "Ecdysiast." Mr. Fry became a man of action after attending five classes. The course included an all-male weekend camping retreat deep in the woods where they dance naked around a bonfire until their pubic hair burns off. Jake picked a wrong time to bully him and paid dearly for it.

"I'm very well aware of the commotion my bold action has caused," Mr. Fry addressed the class. "It will serve as a message to all students that we teachers aren't to be trifled with." I wonder what will happen to Jake. Dad said, without education, he might get a low-respecting job, such as a working as a tax auditor for Revenue Canada.

Despite the fact we're free from Jake's reign of brutal terrorism, gym class was the same as usual with Alfonsino looking like a ball boy without his balls. We played Australian rules football upon the muddy field in the cold rain. Evidently, Mr. Barracuda was wallowing in his "my-gerbil-is-missing-and-there-is-a-homicidal-maniac-with-a-hedge-trimmer-on-the-loose" mood.

A second student was expelled today! Headmaster Sculpin burst into our Latin class and bellowed, "Peter!" Our hair shot straight up. The headmaster was waving a certain picture of an old nun.

"What is the meaning of this?" Headmaster Sculpin read out loud the writing on the corner, "This is for you sir, from Peter Guppy." Pornography earns an automatic expulsion. This will shut every one up about my "hot dog" incident.

After school, I went to the hearing aid specialist to pick up my new molds. After wearing old rock-hard molds for the last few weeks, the new flexible ones feel so good in my ears.

Mum is still watching TV in the dingy basement as I write this. The chess-by-mail championship is still on; she didn't even bother changing the channel.

Friday night is finally here! Every night I've been imagining Demoiselle and me dancing under the stars to romantic love songs. I'll go to bed early tonight so tomorrow will come around faster.

Saturday, May 28: Pre-dance. I woke up this morning at 7:45 a.m. bushy-eyed and wide-tailed. I was too excited about the dance tonight to correct my phrase and go back to sleep. I rested in bed for several minutes, watching the sun-tipped clouds pass by my window, feeling warm waves of bliss washing over me. After a good breakfast of Donkey Kong cereal, I enthusiastically did my homework all afternoon (this hardly ever happens). I cooperated with Mrs. Tautog, didn't even try to spit when she asked me to say "Pith." When I told her about the date tonight, she advised, "You should tell the girl about your hearing impairment, you cannot hide it forever." Ya right. She also gave me ridiculous advice such as when I'm with my love, I should sit away from the loudspeakers in a quiet, well-lit place so I could read her lips better. Where the hell can I find such a place? In a motel room down the street?

At 4:00 p.m., I stopped my homework, took a shower and dressed in my best clothes. I carefully brushed my hair to hide my hearing aids and hair-sprayed it to keep it in place. It's 6:50, it's finally time to go to the dance. I can barely contain my excitement—I would be seeing Demoiselle in less than an hour! I'll write more when I get back.

Post-dance. Dad dropped me off in front of the gym and I stepped inside to begin what was the most wonderful night of my life. Demoiselle came in at exactly 7:47, looking radiant as ever when our eyes met across the room. Her face lit up with a broad smile as she strode straight to me. She cheerfully greeted me with a loud, "Hi!" and gave me a nice arms-wrapped-around-my back hug. My muscles instantly became wobbly, my heart thumped faster and my head felt airy.

Demoiselle put her hand on my arm and said, "Hey, I heard that someone at your school was caught masturbating in front of some nuns." I didn't reply. She led me to the worst place to sit down: next to an amplifier the size of refrigerator and behind a bright light, the kind military ships use to communicate with other ships. She babbled on and on, her face heavily silhouetted and I squinted in an extraordinary effort to read her lips. Not only that, the music was loud enough to make any sweet nothings into a nothing. I couldn't understand her at all. I nodded a lot and muttered, "Oh really?" at anything that appeared interesting from the looks of her shaded face. At one point, she pointed to someone in the crowd and continued to babble nonsensically.

"Nice," I murmured, clueless. I only managed to make out a few words out of the thousands she blathered. Now I think of it, I may have ominously heard the words, "Lamprey Snow," the same name her father mentioned in our tortured phone conversation. Other than this, the rest of the night was a dream. She finally stopped chattering, and I, a soon-to-be RCAF pilot, danced with her, a soon-be-RCAF-pilot's-wife, to every slow song, holding each other closely. From all my dance experiences I've had, I never had a girl hold me with such true feeling before. I closed my eyes and savoured every passing minute. I began to hate the clock for advancing so fast.

We even danced the fast songs in between, her beautiful smiling eyes gazing into mine. We sat down to rest at one point and watched Alfonsino dance. Stuffed in a strategic place down his checkered bell-bottomed pants, as he told me earlier, was a rather large cucumber. This may have something to do with his belief that, "If woman can have push-up bras, us men can have push-up underwear, too." After a number of finger-jabbing-in-the-air moves and hip wriggling among embarrassed girls, he began doing this funny squatting dance and I saw it: the cucumber had slid down and was jiggling around in the seat of his pants. With each dance move, the cucumber slowly slid down his pants leg. He did these Rockette kicking moves in a vain attempt to get the cucumber back up and after one hard kick, it shot out his pants and hit an innocent bystander in the back of her head. In an effort to distract people from the fallen vegetable, he did a bad Russian dance. Girls backed away from him while glancing at the exit.

The clock then read 10:45 p.m., 15 minutes away from the end of the greatest dance of all time. The guitar from

"Stairway to Heaven" began to strum and Demoiselle and I merged our bodies, enveloped by the last slow song of the night. I closed my eyes and let myself be wrapped by her warm embrace. I remember opening my eyes and seeing the star lights arc the walls, my classmates in their own love worlds and Alfonsino on his knees begging an embarrassed but ugly girl to dance with him.

After the song's dying words melted into the haze, the harsh gym lights went up. The greatest dance was over. We blinked at each other in the bright lights for a few seconds and she bent forward and gave me a long kiss on the lips. My socks were knocked off! The kiss felt natural, as if I've been doing this all my life. I'm now a man! As I write this, my hands are still trembling. It's 12:45 and it's time to sleep and dream of fresh clouds, love and kisses.

Sunday, May 29: Woke up this morning feeling refreshed and comfortably warm from last night's dream. I rested in bed for another hour, recreating everything about last night, especially the kiss. After years of watching mushy kisses on TV and saying "Yuck" when I was a kid, I now understand its appeal. I won't look at another kiss the same way again now that I have joined the exclusive club of the kissed.

One dark cloud was something I left unmentioned in yesterday's journal entry. I guess I was so enamored with the wonderful night that I didn't think twice about it. When Demoiselle and I walked outside after the dance, a scruffy guy in a leather jacket grabbed her by the arm and said something. Demoiselle yelled at him for a short while and ended her piece with, "Bug off, eh?" but the word "Bug" had four letters. The guy answered back with shouted words. Demoiselle chose to ignore him and we continued walking. Perturbed, Demoiselle looked at me and said, "He's just a blah blah blah." This was all I caught and she said nothing more about it. At that time, I quickly pushed the incident out of my mind as I walked to the corner with her and she hugged me goodnight before getting into her father's car. Who was that guy?

I stopped by to see Luderick on my way to the store to buy more breath mints but he was again quiet and reflective. "Sorry man—my mom is getting my goat about this Church thing. She wants me to join the choir! 'So you can be closer to God' she says." Thankfully he refused because his singing is worse than the sounds of a banjo hitting a yodelling Mexican nationalist with a blocked nose.

I wanted to call Demoiselle but Mum was out all night with Dad.

Monday, May 30: When I walked by the gym on my way to school this morning, the warm feelings from Saturday night's dance flooded back. I stared momentarily at the spot where I last saw Demoiselle before she entered her father's car. The gym building has a special feeling associated with it. Before, it was only an ordinary brick building where Mr. Barracuda yells at us to grow chest hair and commit classmaticide and it's now a building filled with warmth, love and paradise. For now.

I remembered something. My blissful smile disappeared and the warm feelings were shot away into the cold darkness. I had an awful flashback of the leather-jacketed guy. I can see him step out of the shadows in slow motion and grab Demoiselle. She turned around, her hair swishing by and mouthing something to the offender. Somewhere in this slo-mo action in my mind, I saw the words "Lamprey" on her lips. Why is this name giving me chills? I snapped out of the flashback and shook my head to free myself from the awful image. I mentally crumpled the picture up into a tight ball and threw it violently into the wastepaper basket in my mind that has a sticker, "Unconscious mind—Made in Austria." Successfully repressing the memory, I continued walking once I began to feel good about that wonderful Saturday night.

The talk of Jakes' departure and rumours that he'll work as a mafia thug have died down and school is back to normal. Mr. Fry is much more relaxed and the vein in his neck no longer throbs during his lectures. However, I couldn't fully savour Jake's absence because my new hearing molds were bothering me all afternoon. When I took them out, I felt inside my ears and found traces of blood! The new molds were not made perfectly and have been rubbing my ears raw. I asked Mum to make another appointment with the hearing aid specialist and I exchanged the molds for old ones as a temporary replacement.

After supper, with plans to ask Mum to call my beloved, I went into the kitchen to find her talking to Mora. I saw several brochures spread all over the table, all from assorted colleges. What are they for? I wasn't able to have a good view because I bolted when Mum shot me The Look. I'll ask her to call tomorrow.

Tuesday, May 31: I found more college brochures on our kitchen table and asked Dad about them but he doesn't know what Mum is doing and thought the brochures were mine. We asked her about them at the supper table, but she was evasive. "Don't look at a gift horse in the wrong end."

Mum went out again! She came back home at 10:30 p.m. and said it was too late to call Demoiselle. "Ya don't wanna wake up her grumpy father, ya know." I agreed.

June

Wednesday, June 1st: It's June already and the last day of classes is only two weeks away. Ever since I got the horrible mark in public speaking last week, my mind is preoccupied about failing (when not preoccupied with Demoiselle). Failing has several awful implications: 1) I won't graduate with my class; 2) Canterbury will kick me out and I'll have to re-do secondary 5 in public school; and worse of all, 3) I won't be able to go to the prom with Demoiselle. All this threatens my dream of owning a simple suburban home with a golf-green lawn, a flowerpot in the kitchen and a Spitfire plane in the garage. I may have to consider a cardboard box as my next possible real estate purchase. I've one more speech left to do on the last week of class, an epic 15-minute final oral presentation worth 50% of the final grade. I calculated if I don't get at least 87%, I will fail public speaking class and ultimately, high school.

I read a newspaper article reporting that Freebob representatives are heading to Canada to recruit new members. Freebobs have a shared belief in assorted conspiracies and a high degree of mistrust in authority. Their sworn enemies are: government officials, banks, CIA, FBI, ATF, any other organization with three letters, the entire police force and, most strangely, people who own donut shops. They live in extreme suspicion of them and often have an uncomfortable feeling that they're being watched by squirrels hiding in trees. Their primary activities include not paying taxes, hoarding slingshots, ringing doorbells and running away and squeezing toothpaste back into the tube.

The article reported that the RCMP have been tracking the Freebobs' movements in Toronto. "We will watch them closely," Chief Lingcod said. "We shall protect our Canadian citizens from the group's insidious influence."

Mum and I called Demoiselle tonight and again, I spoke to her while she interpreted. We talked a bit and I asked if she can go out this Saturday, but she was busy.

"Sorry, I really wish I could but I have to visit my grandfather in the hospital this weekend and it's far away in Lac-au-Brochet."

She didn't sound as cheerful as she was at the dance. Before we bade goodbye, she said she'll write me a letter. Mum commented that she heard another voice in the background, a female voice.

"Maybe it was her sister," she thought out loud.

Thursday, June 2: My old temporary replacement molds, loose as they are, are driving me nuts. The appointment with the hearing aid specialist is tomorrow but I don't think I could stand another day of this inane whistling.

I read a news item that the Freebobs converted a few gullible Torontonians by luring them with a free subscription to the "*Financial Post*."

"It was an unavoidable situation," said Chief Lingcod, "the subscription offer came with free watch-calculator."

Friday, June 3: For gym, we again played Australian Rules football in the dark pouring rain under Mr. Barracuda's orders. He must've been wallowing in his "my-goldfish-died-and-the-oven-light-bulb-is-out" melancholia. Not wanting to subject my hearing aids to water torture, I put them in my gym locker, a mistake that played a role in an embarrassing incident on the field. Before I get to this, I have to say it was a strange experience, playing the game and hearing no sounds: classmates' mouth open and close in pain as bodies slam to each other, Mr. Barracuda's beet-red face contorting and the flashing ambulance zipping by in absolute silence. I felt truly deaf.

The embarrassing moment: I was on the shirtless team, the score was tied and a minute remained in the game. The other team was near our goal line during a scrum, threatening to make a winning score. Under the cone of silence, I was on the periphery of the circular mass of writhing wet bodies jostling for the over-inflated football. As the ball bounced around, the half-naked bodies slid around in the mud and the ball popped out in front of me. With nothing but an empty field behind me, I grabbed it and ran for my dear life across the whole field towards the goal line. I vaguely felt splashes behind me—someone was after me! With the rain beating against my pale chest, my heart in my throat and feet slapping against the muddy grass, I sped with gusto. I'm going to be a hero! I spurted to the goal line, slid and touched the ball to the ground. Goal! We win! I stopped hooting and pumping my arms when I noticed that none of my teammates have mobbed their new hero. I looked to my near left and saw Mr. Barracuda bending over, out of breath and his bald spot gleaming wet. Far down the field, I saw my classmates' faces contorted in laughter. Huh? After a few moments of knee slapping and pointing, everyone trotted off to the showers, shaking their heads in amusement. Once I put my hearing aids back on after our shower, Alfonsino slapped me on my back and guffawed, "Good entertainment, Egg. I couldn't have done it better myself."

Bill Bream didn't tell me the meaning of all this until we walked to class. "Egg, Mr. Barracuda had already blown the whistle to stop the play. He was about to bend down to pick up the ball when you grabbed it from him and took off down the field. He chased you all the way down, huffin' and puffin', waving his arms and screaming, 'Egg, stop! Give the damn ball back!' You just kept running. What guts. And oh—your victory dance—oh man, that was hilarious."

For biology, Mr. Fry assigned an interesting home project related to the current subject of bacteria culture and how they develop. Our final assignment was to take a piece of cheese, bread and small amount of yogurt and put it aside near a window where the sun shines. In a week or so, we should be seeing the food change colour and go fuzzy as the bacteria multiply. On the last week of school, we have to bring in our specimens, along with a three-page report on how the bacteria culture develops. I placed the cheese, bread and yogurt in separate containers on my bedroom windowsill by a large sign that read, "Don't eat, biology project." The last time I did a similar project, Dad ate it and became so sick and delirious that he tried to set Mum's houseplants free in our backyard. I still remember him bending over in his bathrobe and urging the upended plants, "Run, run, go to your brothers!"

After school, I went to see Mr. Halibut the hearing aid specialist about fixing my new molds. He looked at the offending pieces, turning them over in his fingers with a frown on his face and deduced, in best professional tone of voice, "Oops. I gave you the wrong molds." After scrounging around his overfilled desk, turning over papers, pushing aside hearing aid-related parts, he piped up, "Ah—there they are!" He found my new molds in his pita sandwich. "Here," he said, wiping off the garlic hummus. "These are yours, they should fit better." They do feel better except for the weird smell. I'll have to slather the molds with mouthwash the next time I see Demoiselle in case she, in throes of passion, tries to nibble on my earlobes.

Saturday, June 4: At the dinner table, Dad was telling us one of his usual case histories about a guy with multiple personality disorder whose analyst charged him for group therapy when Mum interrupted.

"I've somethin' to tell y'all—I'm goin' back to school! I'm jest tired of bouncin' from job to job with few skills. I jest want a job I would stick with n' enjoy," she said assertively. She will study dental hygiene in college. Ilisha and Dad agreed and fully supported her decision but I was dismayed. Mum? In school? This means we both will be in college at the same time!

I read in the *Montreal Star* that the Freebobs have left Toronto and were seen travelling towards Montreal by train. Chief Lingcod remarked, "We suspect they were unhappy with the lack of bars and the ten p.m. closing time."

I looked up from the newspaper to see Mum inspecting my hair from the entrance of the kitchen. "Yer hair is long. Come 'n sit 'ere and I'll go git my scissors."

I paused for a second, pursing my lips. "No way mum, not this time." It was the first time I've refused this. She stood back, smiled and left at that.

Sunday, June 5: I went over to see Luderick this afternoon and his mother answered the door with a somber expression. This wasn't new—the woman would look somber even if she found a wide-open parking space in front of the downtown bank.

"Good afternoon, Egg," she mouthed as if she was doing jaw exercises, "I have bad news. Luderick left home yesterday and have joined that evil cult the Freebobs." My face dropped. "Come in Egbert and join me in prayer for his lost soul, we need to pray long and hard to the almighty God and Jesus the savior." she said, motioning me toward the prayer room. "Uh, no thanks Mrs. Bass, I've got to go home to paint the deck." I left before she could say another word.

Damn! I should've known! Why didn't I see this coming? When a group seeped in conspiracies and paranoia comes by, Luderick would be attracted to it like a horny dog to a leg. I can't believe it—my best friend is gone. Will I ever see him again? He'd better resist all attempts to be brainwashed—he still owes me five bucks.

Monday, June 6: When English literature class was finished, Mr. Coley asked me to stay behind. He shuffled to the front of his desk and leaned against it. "Mr. Flounder, what do you aspire to be?"

"A Royal Canadian Air Force pilot, sir."

"Hmmm, what about a career in writing?" He coughed.

"Well, I want to be a pilot, it's more exciting."

He put a gentle hand on my shoulder, looked at me in the eye and said, "You're a good writer, Mr. Flounder, one of the best I've seen in my 30 years here."

"Thanks sir, but I still want to be a pilot."

Mum was right about my hair. It did look unkempt and awful (a by-product of a bad haircut by a depressed ex-hairdresser last month). For the first time in my young life, I went to a hair salon in the shopping centre by myself—no appointment for Mum to make, no complicated four-page forms to fill out and no waiting for my name to be called.

The receptionist led me to an empty salon chair and introduced me to the hair stylist: it was none other than Molly!

"Hi, Eggie, how are you today?" she queried as she draped the black cape around my neck and shoulders. I could smell her sweet perfume.

"Uh, good," I choked. Sitting in the "Ol' Sparky" electric chair in a Texas prison would've been more comfortable. Two thoughts came to mind: 1) what if Demoiselle sees me with her? And, 2) by cutting in close quarters to my ears, she'll see my hearing aids and my cover will be blown in no time flat. When Mum cuts my hair, I always took them out but if I do the same with Molly, how will I hear her if she chats with me like the hairdressers do on TV? After instructing her to keep the hair long around my ears, Molly turned around to get her scissors. I took this opportunity to yank out my hearing aids and hide them under the cape. As Molly began to cut my hair, I kept my eyes trained to the mirror to watch her lips to detect any signs of movement that would necessitate the use of my super lip-reading powers and respond in a mumbled reply. The governor called the Texas prison and I was given a reprieve! She didn't say a single word throughout the job. I daresay it was strange but arousing to have another woman delicately touch and handle my hair. A few times, I strayed from my lip-watching mission because her bosoms were inches from my face, but I kept on the task. I've never been this close to boobs since I was breast-fed as a baby. (My future psychoanalyst will have a field day with this comment.) When she was finished, Molly smiled sensually as she stood behind me with a hand-mirror so I could see the back of my head. She did an excellent job: my sides were even, my ears were not nicked and my hair wasn't traumatized.

Another problem was putting my hearing aids back in when she was done. I decided to stuff them in my pants and nonchalantly pay the bill in complete silence. I watched the cash register, and when I saw it came to $12.00, I pulled out a twenty from my jeans and one of my hearing aids flew out and landed in the candy bowl in front of Molly. Before she could see it, I shot my hand out to grab the hearing aid and popped it in my mouth. Yech—it tasted like garlic.

"You need to make a donation, dear Eggie," her mouth said in silence. I read the sign in front of the candy bowl and it was for guide dogs for the blind. I put in 50 cents. I should've donated the white cane I took in that face-plant and stumble off the bus back in January. I gave her a five-dollar tip and she beamed a grateful smile and rubbed my back. "Thank you so much, Eggie," Next time I'll give her ten bucks.

I plugged in my hearing aids and had to eat two breath-mints to get rid of the taste of waxy garlicky molds. On the bright side, Demoiselle didn't catch me with Molly—she would've taken a Beretta and blown my nuts off for sure.

I read an item buried in the back of the *Montreal Star* reporting that the Freebobs have left the country with several of their newest recruits, one of them being my friend Luderick.

Chief Lingcod reported, "The victims from Montreal were lured with fraudulent offers of free bagels and Montreal Canadiens tickets."

The reporter managed to interview the group's leader before their departure at the Dorval airport.

"We achieved our objective and are happy with our new members, " the guru said, "although one guy keeps complaining about American TV shows and our use of snooze alarms."

Tuesday, June 7: It was announced that our English literature teacher, Mr. Coley, is on leave for the rest of the year for "health reasons." I was the last to see him yesterday and he looked fine to me. Headmaster Sculpin took over the class for the day and taught us about "the wonderful world" of predicates, independent clauses and adverbs. Evidently, this was his version of English literature.

At lunchtime, my classmates were jabbering excitedly, the conversation bouncing from one bobbing head to the next, voices overlapping and people finishing each other's sentences.

"What's going on?" I asked Bill Bream.

"Jake was picked up by the police yesterday afternoon as a suspect in an armed robbery!"

Apparently, a man fitting his description walked into a Tout-Epicerie late last night, put a $20 bill on the counter and asked for change. When the clerk opened the cash drawer, he pulled out a gun and asked for all the cash in the register, which the clerk promptly gave. The man took the cash and fled, leaving the $20 bill on the counter. You want to know the total amount of cash he took? Fifteen dollars. What a stupid doofus! Now, a question: if someone points a gun at you and gives you money, was a crime committed?

Since my final public speaking test is next Tuesday, I made an effort to find out what my assigned topic is going to be. This time, it wasn't an odd topic such as, "19th century toilet seat covers," "Garden Leek," or "The reproductive capacity of thumbtacks." Mr. Bonito told me that I have to give a historical account of a female Czechoslovakian author, which sounds as exciting as watching wood warp. Alfonsino was assigned a more boring topic, "Eighteenth century poems about shoes."

Tonight, Dad cooked dinner for the two of us because Mum and Ilisha were out. Not a good thing; he's one of those guys who relies on the smoke detector to tell him when dinner's ready. It took forever to chew on what resembled lumps of coal on my plate.

"Good supper, Dad," I commented, "it's cleaning out my bowels."

In between bites, a strange question from Dad: "My lad, have you ever considered learning sign language some day?"

I put down my mystery lump of something. "Uh, no. I can talk, so why learn sign language?"

"Hmm," he said thoughtfully, pushing another blackened lump in his mouth.

Wednesday, June 8: I was saddened by Mr. Coley's absence today. His replacement was a nerdy-looking guy with a high slope of cowlick in the middle of his forehead. From a certain angle it resembled a tidal wave about to crush a small Japanese village. I could imagine a tiny boat at the bottom of wave with two screaming flea-sized Japanese fishermen. He marched in class without a word and with a ridiculous stern expression on his face, he wrote his name on the blackboard in big block letters so big Russians would've been able to read it from their satellite photographs:

MR. FINN

He repeated his name out loud, as if the chalk dust had blinded us, "I'm Mr. Finn, I'll be replacing Mr. Coley for the rest of the term in this English class." What a career move—he has only one week left to teach.

"The name is Mr. Finn, I don't want to hear any vulgar rhymes, references to body parts, or anything remotely associated with fishes in connection with my name. So that aside—class, tell me what the esteemed Mr. Coley had taught you so far," he said. This is so he could pick up where the ex-teacher left off, he explained. We told him about our weekly assignment in free-form writing, how he would read passages from different books and that he talked to us about our future aspirations (this one was from me).

"Wh-what-what about Shakespeare?"

We shook our heads no.

"The poems of Robert Frost?"

More head shaking and shoulder shrugs.

"Literary devices such as bildungsromanism? Deux ex machina? Polysyndetons?"

No head shaking this time—total sea of blank faces.

"Did Mr. Coley follow the English literature curriculum at all?" As if a bunch of 17 year-old guys would know. Mr. Finn sank into a realization that Mr. Coley hasn't taught us anything of real utility in the past nine months except proper essay writing techniques. Mr. Finn began to look dizzy and practically collapsed in his chair.

After several seconds of silence, he got his bearings and spoke up, "Listen, there is a governing body called, 'The School Board' (he made obnoxious quotation marks with his fingers) who ascertains that every course in the curriculum meets with prescribed standards of academia set forth by the Minister of Education. The students have to demonstrate competency in English literature by passing a school board-approved final exam," he intoned as if he memorized the regulation booklet last night.

Mr. Finn sighed deeply and with deadpan expression, said, "This means I cannot devise an exam only testing your skills on writing damn stories!"

To obtain the school board's approval, Mr. Finn is required to compose an exam with questions about Shakespeare, literary devices, poem analysis and such.

"Since Mr. Coley didn't teach properly, how will you pass the exam? If the class fails...then," Mr. Finn made a long pause. "The school board won't allow this class to graduate." A heavy gasp pierced the class air. Chaos exploded forth with much talking, weeping, arguing and suicide attempts.

"They can't do this! It's not our fault!" we shouted at tsunami-hair teacher.

With outstretched arms, Mr. Finn quieted the class and scolded, "If you boys had alerted Headmaster Sculpin a long time ago about Mr. Coley's incompetency, then none of this would've happened." I felt insulted; Mr. Coley was a good man, not incompetent at all.

I began to hate his sloping cowlick—he doesn't care about us! We left class drained and in shock. The possibility of us not graduating hit us hard and was the topic for the rest of the day.

I don't see how I would be able to graduate by doing the incredible feat of passing the English final and getting at least 87% on my epic speech next Tuesday. What about college? My future in flying relic WWII planes? Aviation school administrators aren't going to look too kindly at applicants who re-did a high school grade and answered, "A pear-flavoured milkshake" to the question, "Who was Shakespeare?" My future is starting to look as ugly as a grimy beggar's teeth.

Speaking of changes, I still think about Luderick and wonder how he's doing in the Freebob commune. Is he happy? Has he found his home? Is he learning new conspiracies?

Thursday, June 9: More news about Jake: he confessed to committing the armed robbery. The police interrogated him by placing a metal colander on his head and connecting it with wires to a light bulb. They pressed a hidden button each time they thought he wasn't telling the truth. Believing the "lie detector" was bona fide thing, Jake confessed.

Mr. Finn tersely informed us that he had a meeting with the school's administrators last night and the result is that he must give us the final exam regardless. The only course of action is to do an intensive four-day course on every important aspect of English literature that will be on the final. In addition to his regular classes, Mr. Finn will hold extra after-school classes. To me, it'll be the same as a Formula 1 driver trying to learn from Mandarin language tapes in fast-forward in his car during the last lap.

"In this regard, it's my duty as your teacher to inform you of your rights. You're not required by law to attend those classes after school as they will exceed your allotted number of school hours, but I *strongly* advise you to show up." I don't know how he did it, but when he said, "strongly advise," he said it in a tone that implied, "Or else you will fail and become cotton-pickers in a faraway field in Ecuador." It was effective: every one showed up.

On a whim, I bought a new CF-18 Hornet model, a reward to myself to work on when school is finally over.

I examined my biology project on my room window and it looks bad, but in a good way. The bread has grown stale and is sprouting multi-coloured fuzz. The cheese slice has turned a dark shade of green and the yogurt has little yellow and red islands of fur. It did this in time—the project is due tomorrow. Ten minutes before doing this journal entry, I finished writing the required ten-page research report.

Friday, June 10: I made a mistake about the final biology project: it wasn't due today but next Tuesday. Originally, the deadline was due today, but I didn't catch Mr. Fry's announcement of the change. Since I took care to bring my biology project to school, I didn't want to risk destroying it by carrying it back home and then back to school again on Tuesday. I asked the secretary if she could keep them in the faculty refrigerator for the weekend.

We had our last gym class today and it was the most unusual one in my history at Canterbury. We didn't do the usual such as trying to rip our classmate's arm out its socket, incurring permanent brain damage, or using tongue depressors in a forcible manner. In fact, we didn't even wear our gym clothes.

Mr. Barracuda intercepted us before going into the changing rooms and barked, "Keep your clothes on, men!" He marched us to a vacant classroom down the hall, innocent cows to a slaughterhouse. We were not met with horror, but were treated with kindness, honesty and empathy. He sat on the desk, his whistle beside him and talked to us about our futures. He emphasized that, "What you do today will influence what will happen tomorrow."

Mr. Barracuda told us about his background: he's a happily married man with three young children and his hobby is reading science-fiction novels and model shipbuilding. He was born and raised in a small farming town of Salmon Arm, BC before our school hired him. This is unlike my original image of him as an angry, depressed bachelor living in a grubby one-room apartment across from a flashing hotel sign. At the end of the class, he fell silent, wiped a welling tear and said, "I never meant harm in those sports. Please take care of yourself after leaving high school. You have only one body and mind." As we filed out, he gave each of us a warm handshake and wished us luck. His last words were, "And I don't want to see you back here!" You might, I thought.

At lunchtime, I heard my classmates again talking excitedly about something and all I could catch was the words "rent," "bowtie" and most mysteriously, "caviar." I asked Bill Bream to fill me in and he said, "Don't you know? Our prom is next Saturday."

"But how can we go if we don't graduate?" I asked.

"Doesn't matter, they won't know if we pass or fail until afterwards. So we all will still go!"

The prom! Another thing to freak about! I got to call Demoiselle before someone else takes her, like Warren Beatty. No time to go to the library to study scholarly journal articles on prom protocols, I must call her tonight.

We stayed after school for an extra three hours with Mr. Finn, on a Friday, no less. I tried to imagine myself as a captured RCAF pilot in a P.O.W. camp, digging out rocks, dirty and bleeding from being whipped. However, I couldn't picture ridiculous Mr. Finn as the German guard without giggling.

After a late dinner, I called Demoiselle with my wonderful maternal interpreter by my side. After a polite chitchat, I asked her if she would like to go to the prom with me. An ominous pause followed my question.

"Um, um, O.K., sure," she uttered.

We took the next 25 minutes to work out the details, which was more complicated than biochemistry of Epinephrine in Arabic. Apparently, we won't be the only ones going to the dance together. Her friends and their dates rented a limo and we had to work out the order by which the driver was to pick us up. The driver will also take us to a private party after the dance. After 15 minutes of her explaining the whole shebang, I told her, "I'll just wait for the car to pick me up at 6:35 p.m. and I'll follow you from there." I had other questions, but the problem with having your mother interpret your phone conversations is that you cannot mention forbidden phrases such as, "I'll bring the condoms", "Is there going to be booze at the party?" and "I once stopped a fan with my tongue." Everything has to be censored for delicate mothers' ears.

While I was listening to her, I had the urge to tell Demoiselle that I loved her, but I held my tongue.

Come to think of it, I've never said, "I love you" to a girl before. It's about time for me to express my feelings for her and I'll do it at the prom when the moment is right. First, I must practise it in front of the mirror because I want to get it right the first time and not say, "Hockey stick."

Saturday, June 11: Fueled with worry about my failing schoolwork, I did serious work this afternoon. After a good two hours of solid concentration, I half-finished the CF-18 Hornet model. I've plenty of time to study tomorrow.

Before I went to bed, I practised saying, "I love you" in front of the bathroom mirror but found no good way to say it. Geez, I looked so cheesy.

Sunday, June 12: I slept until 11:30 a.m. and worked on my new plane model all afternoon. I miss seeing my only friend Luderick on those lazy Sunday afternoons, our long talks and playing ball hockey. While reminiscing, it hit me: the oral presentation! I must research, write, proofread, re-write and memorize my presentation about a female Czechoslovakian author for tomorrow! With an hour to spare, I ran to the library.

However, I was de-railed. On the way to the library, a silver sports car pulled up beside me and the electric window on the passenger side slid down. I peered in the window to be greeted by the sight of Molly sitting in the driver's seat. I guess this means she now has her licence and won't need older men to chauffeur her around anymore.

"Hi Eggie darling! I really need your help, come in the car." My heart fluttering and my mind blank, I got in. The car smelled of stale cigarettes. Years of mother's warnings about getting into stranger's cars went out the window along with the tree car freshener. Molly put her hand on my lap and said something.

"Say again?" I squeaked, tearing my eyes away from her hand.

"I need you to buy cigarettes, the bitch at the dépanneur won't sell it to me—she knows I'm under 18. You look 18, she doesn't know you, so can you be a sweetie and get me a pack of Cranec lights?" My Superego, the morality part of my mind, was shouting, "No, no, no, Demoiselle is your girlfriend and you have to go to the library!" but the Id, the pleasure part of my mind, threw Logic and Reason out the window to join the tree freshener and I found myself being driven to the store. Molly went through three stop signs and jumped the curb as she drove up the store. I wondered at this point if I should ask to see her driver's licence. "I'll wait here, Eggie darling" she said and winked sensually.

Zombie-like, I entered the store and standing behind the counter was Mum's friend and neighbour, Mora. Damn. In a distant cemetery for doofs, a gravedigger picks up his shovel. "Hi Egbert, stopping by to get your mother's TV Guide?"

"Uh—no, uh, a pack of Cranec lights, please." I couldn't believe I was hearing those words coming from me. The gravedigger starts shovelling.

Mora frowned, "Well, you're not 18 yet, dear." I glanced about, my mind scrambling for a good explanation. I could see Molly outside, her fingers tapping on the steering wheel.

"Oh, it's not for me, ha ha, it's for a science project I'm doing on lung cancer." The gravedigger digs deeper.

"Oh yeah?" Mora's eyes lit up, "Tell me more." I gave an elaborate explanation of the project—the posters, the beaker with cigarette smoke, the artificial lung and the oxygen reader—the whole works. The grave is now six feet deep. She turns around and hands me a small pack of Cranec lights. I scrounged around my pockets and paid 2 bucks.

"Why did you get such a small pack?" Molly complained when I handed her the box. Seeing my panicky eyes, she waved it off. "Never mind, this will do for now." She didn't say "Thank you" nor pay me back the two dollars. At least her hands touched mine when I handed her the pack. After going through more stop signs, zipping through the school zone at 65 km/hr and nearly running over a poor squirrel, she dropped me off the library. I thanked her for the ride (and thanked my lucky stars that I made it in one piece). I walked up the library and pulled on the door—locked! I looked at the posted hours and my stomach dropped—it had closed twelve minutes ago! Damn! The Tree freshener, Logic and Reason pushed my zombie body into the grave.

I scooted home, skipped supper and managed to write an adequate speech using research information gleaned from my trusty *"Children's Illustrated Dictionary."* I worked until 4:58 a.m. perfecting it.

Monday, June 13: My oral presentation papers were stolen this morning! I was walking towards my bus stop, re-reading the presentation when I bumped into a large stomach. I craned my neck up to see the owner of the stomach.

Jake!

"You go where the sun not shine," he rumbled and his belly jiggled. Vocabulary was never his strong suit.

"Jake! Aren't you supposed to be in jail for some grocery store robbery?"

"Bail!" He roared and his baseball mitt-sized paws lashed out. I raised my arms in self-defense and he knocked the papers out of my hands.

I took a wise course of action and followed his advice: I bailed.

My spindly legs whipping under me, I quickly distanced myself far from Jake, whose lumbering body didn't make it past the corner. I sprinted several blocks to the bus terminus and breathlessly boarded the waiting bus. When I sat down, I slapped my forehead—I left my presentation papers behind!

Mr. Bonito was never going to accept the excuse that my homework was left behind in quivering fear after meeting this banished student. Thankfully, the class was in the forth period and this gave me time to re-write a new presentation during class. However, my knee-knocking encounter with the former Canterbury classmate had reduced my memory of the epic 15-minute oral presentation to a few piddling words. I invented a new "history" to describe the life of one "famous" Patty Rasbora, around those few words I remembered. I ad-libbed, spoke off the cuff, winged it, flew by the seat of my pants and bullcrapped my way through the presentation.

Mr. Bonito was pleased and gave me 88%! I passed!

At lunchtime, I asked the school secretary to retrieve my biology project from the staff refrigerator and she returned saying, "It's not there anymore." It's gone! Damn! Someone must've thrown it out. In my intensive search for a substitute at home, I found mysterious life forms that have been lurking in the back of our 'fridge since the Pierre Trudeau administration. It looks over-done in a bacteria sense, but it'll do.

Mr. Finn is sick! He woke up feeling ill on Saturday morning, attributed to his eating "a bad lunch" on the day before. Headmaster Sculpin acted as the substitute teacher for a substitute teacher in the "Learn everything about English literature in four days" class using the material Mr. Finn had sent him. He even taught the after-school class. He's more boring than Mr. Finn. He looked at my FM system microphone as if it was a bizarre curio and wore it upside-down.

While I was memorizing my Latin verbs, Mum burst into my room, stood over me with her arms crossed. Her face was tense. "Egg, Mora told me that ya bought a pack of cigarettes, are ya smokin' now? She didn't believe that story about some science project." My face felt hot. I could envision the Tree Freshner, Logic, and Reason wagging their fingers saying, "I told you so." I used my car salesman skills and sold her a rusty oil-leaking story of how I wanted to experiment with cigarettes, tried one puff, suffered a deathly coughing fit, vowed to never touch the poison sticks ever again, they were terrible, I was an idiot to try them, it was the stupidest thing I've ever done and so on. I was beating myself up enough so she wouldn't have to do it and it worked—it took the wind out of her sails.

"Oh, ok. I see, don't ya do that again," she scolded lightly before leaving. I was never so happy to see my Latin verbs again.

Tuesday, June 14: Mr. Finn is still sick today and Headmaster Sculpin subsituted again. The principal sighed, "Today is the last class and we still have to cover the literary period between 1756–1891, the entire poetry collection of Margaret Atwood and the 1970s era of Robertson Davies," he informed us at the start of class, his knobby knuckles pressing against the desk.

"Listen carefully." He took a deep breath, closed his eyes for five seconds, and exploded forth with an auctioneer's voice speed, "Margaret Atwood is a famous Canadian author who…", frantically scribbled unreadable notes on the blackboard and showed us three movie adaptations of classic literature in fast-forward. It was a superhuman feat of teaching: trying to cram six volumes of information into the heads of 17-year-old boys who barely remember which side their hair is supposed to part.

At the end of the class, Headmaster Sculpin collapsed in his chair, his white shirt wet with huge armpit stains, chalk powder on his black pants and hair askew. I couldn't keep up and barely wrote any notes. I tried borrowing Bill Bream's notes but he got as far as the date on the top of his notebook. Alfonsino was reduced into a speechless dolt, mumbling incoherently and staring vacantly into space. It's useless. We all are going to fail. I could kiss my first year at aviation college goodbye.

Wednesday, June 15: Today was the last day of school. We had exams all day in each subject and I think I passed them all. How did I do in Mr. Coley/Finn/Sculpin's English exam? It was easy-peasy. You know why? It had nothing to do with Headmaster Sculpin's extraordinary efforts to teach us, our great, unrealized intelligence or whatever. The exam book had the answers in them! The test was multiple-choice format and lo and behold, next to the correct answers was a small asterisk. Since Mr. Finn was sick last weekend, he must've given the answer booklet to the photocopy centre in confusion and delirium.

No one noticed the mistake until it plopped on our desks. Using hand signals, we told each other to scratch off the asterisk so Mr. Finn won't see his error. Mr. Scale, the invigilator, didn't notice our arm waving and hand gestures because he was preoccupied with his mismatched socks and his receding hairline.

The French test was another one for the books. Mr. Poisson asked the students to pass around a blank test sheet with numbered lines and instructed, "Each dictated phrase will have an error either in verb or conjunction. Write down both incorrect and correct phrase. Each phrase will be repeated only twice." I leaned forward, my pencil poised over the paper and upped by lip-reading vision by a few notches. He took out a tape recorder and pressed, "Play." What the hell? He stood there by the desk, looking out to us while the tape dictated garbled French. Five years at Canterbury and he forgets I'm hearing impaired! I was flabbergasted, my head began to pound and my hands trembled over my blank test as my classmates dutifully wrote down each phrase. Bill Bream caught my appalled look and gave me a "relax" gesture. Relax? How? Thoughts of running and jumping through the big classroom window screaming and swan diving onto the lawn below came to mind. I could only sit there and pretend to write something in the blank lines with sinking despair that I'll score a big fat zero.

"Time's up! Put your test on my desk now," Mr. Poisson bellowed and the class stood up and crowded around the desk; Bill grabbed my sheet of nonsense gibberish and gave me a completed sheet with my name on top. "Here, give this to him," Bill mouthed. Apparently, when we were passing around the test sheets, Bill took two and wrote down the phrases on both—one for him and one for me!

I thanked him big time afterwards. Bill brushed my comment aside, "No problem. It wasn't fair at all, it was like asking a paraplegic to do the running long jump for a phys ed test."

I cleaned out my locker with a mixed sense of finality. Is this the last time I'll stumble around in Canterbury's hallways as a graduate or a failure who had to re-do secondary 5 in public school?

Unexpectedly, I decided to call Demoiselle to see how her exams went. With Mum by my side, I dialed the number and her creepy father answered.

"Hello, what do you want?" the gruff voice said, vibrating my ears.

"Good evening sir, may I speak to Demoiselle please?" I squeaked.

"Lamprey, is that you?" he barked.

"No, this is Egg."

"She's not here."

Silence.

I piped up, "Tell her to call me tomorrow night."

He hung up.

Hmmm.

The fridge stopped working and Mum had to throw out almost all the food. She called the repairman and he's coming tomorrow.

Thursday, June 16: I slept until 11:00 a.m. until Mum woke me up. "I hafta leave, you need to wait for th' fridge repairman," She mouthed into my groggy eyes. "Egg, you stay on the main floor all the time 'n listen for the doorbell. An' fer gawd sakes, don't ever turn off yer 'earing aids!" She wriggled the hearing aids in my face.

I dressed and trudged down into the kitchen. The man is supposed to come at precisely between "11:33 a.m. and 4:58 p.m." Wonderful. I parked my butt in the kitchen, ate breakfast (bowl of Pac-man cereal) and worked on my CF-18 Hornet model plane model. I finished it in an hour and 17 minutes but couldn't paint it because the paint was upstairs in my room. I sighed. I must stay on the main floor or else I wouldn't hear the doorbell.

So I ate.

I read the newspaper.

I ate again.

I did the dishes.

I clipped my toenails.

I drank a glass of orange juice.

I counted the hair on the back of my hand. Seventy-three hairs.

I popped my cheeks.

It was only 1:23 and no sign of the repairman. I ate lunch consisting of a peanut butter and banana sandwich and chips. After lunch, I felt sleepy. I slapped myself silly.

I desperately needed the paint for the plane model; painting would eat up an hour or two at least. I stepped out, looked both ways of Malcolm Street and when I was satisfied that the repair guy's van was nowhere to be seen, I made my move. I zipped upstairs to my bedroom and grabbed the— where are they? My box of modelling paint wasn't there! I scrambled around the mess in my room, looked under the pile of dirty clothes, dug out my closet, ripped off my bed sheets—

it's gone! Wait! It's in the basement! I flew down two flights of stairs, rummaged around the workbench, pulled out the drawers left and right—found it! I raced back into the kitchen and began to paint the model. I finished painting the plane under an hour. Still no repairman. The clock read 3:17—sigh.

So I ate.

I doodled on the notepad.

I stared at my cat.

I combed my hair.

I ate again.

I switched socks to the other foot.

At 4:45, Mum came home. She stood in the entrance and stared at a slip of yellow paper in her hand as if it was an eviction notice.

"Egg, did ya stay here like I tol' ya?"

"Uh, pretty much."

"The repairman left dis note," she said as she showed it to me. It read, "No one home, please call for another appointment."

Argh—what a waste of time! If only I didn't need the modelling paint!

Tomorrow is the graduation ceremony, I'll find out if I graduate or not. Not only that, the prom is the day after! I'll wait tonight for Demoiselle to call back.

12:15 a.m. I write this with a heavy hand. Mum and I stayed up all night waiting for my love to call. We sat on the dusty sofa downstairs and watched a 2-hour documentary about a bomb defuser prone to sneezing fits. I spent most of the night with one eye to the TV and the other riveted to the quiet phone. It never rang. I wondered if Demoiselle's father gave her my message?

Friday, June 17: Today officials at Canterbury will mark our examinations, record our grades and mail our final report card. It should arrive sometime next week. I tried sending them telepathic signals—"Pass me, pass me" until I got a headache. I stopped when I realized it wouldn't work. They wouldn't know who "me" is.

I came back from my big graduation ceremony a few minutes ago. Mum, Dad and Ilisha and I first ate at my favourite seafood restaurant, "Something's Fishy" where they gave me a graduation gift—an Avro Arrow airplane model (hope this does not foreshadow a dismantling of my future life) and we went to the school gym for the ceremony. It was strange being in the gym for the last time, a lot of memories here. It's where Mr. Barracuda screamed obscenities, where Jake splattered our blood on the walls and where I fell in love with Demoiselle. We were given black gowns and caps as we entered. Alfonsino was trying to make a move with Kyle's buxom mother, a policewoman who was probably considering a restraining order.

I sat in the section reserved for the graduating class on the left of the platform, the entire faculty sat on the right and the parents sat in the middle. Mr. Coley was there, looking healthy as ever, sitting next to a weak Mr. Finn. I glanced around and noticed that every student was here, even the ones who've surely failed. I had guessed they'll call those who passed, give them their diplomas and leave the failed ones to deal with their grief among friends. Headmaster Sculpin stepped up to the lectern in a gown and gave a long, tedious speech. Damn—I forgot to bring my FM system! I cranked up my hearing aids, focused on reading his portly lips from the side at 50 paces away. Gradually, slowly, imperceptibly, my hearing aid batteries died. I checked my pockets—no spare batteries! I tried lip-reading without sound but gave up after two minutes. He finally stopped but a long-faced old guy came to podium and gave another long speech, and after him, an ugly woman got up, and so on, one endless speech after another, all blowing past my lip-reading radar. I was hot in my gown, my butt was numb and sweaty from the hard plastic chair and my eyes were droopy. This was worse than Church—no gruesome crucifix and no religious scenes on stained glass windows to keep me entertained. Bill Bream, thankfully, was next to me and elbowed me awake whenever my eyes fluttered closed and I began to list to the side. Finally, after a litany of drones, headmaster Sculpin began calling out the names of graduates but from the order the students coming on stage, I noticed it wasn't in alphabetical order. At one point, he called out a name; Sculpin's mouth opening and closing and no one came forward.

"Hey Egg, it's your turn—go!" Bill mouthed as he nudged me. I was overjoyed—I passed! I bounded up the steps and took the diploma and shook Sculpin's wet clammy hands and posed for Dad's camera with my happy idiot grin. I sat back down, wide-awake and pumped. I opened the rolled up parchment and it read:

"THIS IS NOT A DIPLOMA. You will receive the final grades next week and upon successful school board review of your transcript, you will receive your official provincial high school completion diploma. Congratulations!"

What the hell?

"That's how they always did it, handing out fake diplomas

at the ceremony," Bill mouthed. "Because they don't have enough time to mark the final exams."

Damn! And to think I sat there for three hours for a fake diploma!

When we got home, Mum and I agreed to call Demoiselle again tonight. This time her mother answered.

"Who's this?" in a voice that would've raised the hair of the mice chewing on the telephone wires.

"Uh, Egg Flounder, Demoiselle's boyfriend."

"Why are you following me?" in a dreadful shrill tone.

"Following you? What do you mean?"

"Don't play games with me! I saw you taking pictures of me—you and the RCMP and the CSIS!" She said harshly and the mice wet their furry butts.

"I only wanted to speak to Demoiselle."

"Oh go to hell!" in a sharp voice that electrocuted the mice.

"But..." A loud click pierced my hearing aids.

"She hung up," Mum said ruefully.

I think I'll wait for Demoiselle to call back herself.

Disturbed by the call, I worked on the Avro Arrow model and completed the wings. The conversation made me wish I could ask Luderick about the connection between CSIS and taking pictures.

Saturday, June 18: The fridge repairman came at lunchtime and charged my folks extra because it's the weekend. He complained, "I rang the door on Thursday and heard someone running around inside and yelling, '*Tabarnac! Maudit! Câlice!* I was taken back, so I drove off."

Demoiselle finally phoned me! I was in my room doing my model when Ilisha came in.

"Phone, Egg, it's for you. I think it's your girlfriend." Two panicked thoughts snapped through my mind: 1) How did she know? And, 2) Mum wasn't home!

Sensing my panic, she reassured me, "Don't worry, bro. I'll help you." She was as good as Mum. I'm starting to dig my sister—she's not so bad.

Rather than having a nice, long conversation to make up for the missing time between us, all I got was a talk short and quick enough to satisfy the attention span of a 2nd grader in a bioengineering class. In a nutshell, she pretty much said, "I'll see you at the prom. Bye."

All this is puzzling—her delay in calling me, her terse comments and her standoffish manner. Did my hearing aid whistle on the phone? Did she catch my hearing impaired accent? What did I do wrong?

I finished painting the Avro Arrow model and hung it up by the window next to the De Havilland Mosquito WWII model. They looked great next to each other. It would've been even better if a miniature of me was glued into the cockpit. To be realistic, the model pilot would be a skinny stick figure with two clunky hearing aids and would barely see over the instrument panel.

Wednesday, June 22: Checked my mail this afternoon. Nothing from Canterbury. Putting down the mail, it hit me—a tuxedo! I've forgotten to get a tuxedo for the prom! I caught Mum on her way out and asked her borrow her credit card to rent a tux tomorrow.

"Oh Egg! Yer prom is in three days—how are ya gonna to get a nice suit? All the good ones are probably taken by now. Ya know the sayin': If you hurry, you'll get furry."

After puzzling over Mum's latest incomprehensible, I looked up tuxedo rentals in the yellow pages and found a few places I'll go to tomorrow.

Thursday, June 23: Not everything went as planned. I spent the whole day frantically running from one tuxedo rental store to another, hopping on and off the metro about eight times and the bus three times. In the blur of shopping centres, I thought saw Molly and her blond friend in the distance but I was too pre-occupied to seek her out. The results were the same all around: all the tuxes were reserved. Every damn school must be having a damn prom on the same damn night. The only way for me to get a tux is to spring $900 and up for one.

I bumped into Bill Bream at one of the shopping centres I was panicking in. He said that most students already got their report cards in the mail in the last few days.

"If you didn't get yours yet," Bill warned, "it means you might have failed. The school board takes longer to inform those who don't pass because they meet again to re-think their decision to fail someone." A pinball was sent ricocheting off inside my head and my stomach felt as if I had swallowed a drunk Marimba band. Damn.

Arriving home, I burst through the front door and grabbed today's mail on the table. I quickly flipped through the bills and junk mail. My head throbbing and my heart pounding, I checked and rechecked the mail. My back felt hot and sweaty. Nothing! I stared into space.

"Are you all right, dear?" Mum said as she saw me in the hallway, sweaty and clutching the bundle of mail.

"Uh, uh, yeah," I stammered, "I'll be fine in the next two years."

Say, I thought of something: since Luderick joined the Freebob cult before school finished, how is he going to get his diploma without taking the final exams? I should go and join him.

Friday, June 24: I waited in the living room all day for the mailman and the mail was finally delivered at 3:12 pm. Looking through the pile, I found an envelope from Canterbury college and my heart jumped out of my skinny chest. I carried the envelope into the living room, sat away from any sharp implements and open windows and took a few moments to stare at it.

"This is it," I thought. "Here it goes." I ripped open the envelope with trembling fingers and stomach churning as if each organ was fighting over each other to be the first to escape out of my mouth. Unfolding the transcript, my eyes scanned the column of grades—I passed everything! Yes! I'm going to graduate! I noticed my French grade improved by a great deal; I whispered thanks to my wonderful classmate, Bill Bream. Along with the transcript was a letter saying I'll receive my official provincial high school completion diploma in the mail within 4–6 weeks. This is the greatest day of my life! I've so much to look forward to—the prom with Demoiselle tomorrow night, spending the summer with her and our whole post-high school future. I plan to work this summer at what will be my first real job and by September, I'll be going to the aviation school. The only hurdle is passing the entrance interview.

All this was rolled up in a small intense bundle filled with pleasure. Only by looking at those numbers on a piece of paper, I've grown. I don't need facial hair, barn-door shoulders, or large rippling muscles. Manhood is a state of mind and not a mere state of body. My body is a horrible example.

Now I've officially graduated, I still needed a tux. Dad took me to the Salvation Army depot and the only tux they had was a pastel blue suit with lime green ruffles. The previous owner was an 83-year-old man who died last week of cirrhosis of the liver. It was rather tight but it was within my price range: $12.75. At home, I put it on and showed Mum. She freaked out.

"Oh mah gawd," her southern accent worsening with anger, "Are y'really gonna to wear that gawlf suit?"

"It's not a golf suit, Mum," I said hurtfully.

"No self-respecting gal will want to be seen wit' ya."

I looked at myself again in the mirror—my spirits sank like an ex-mobster with cement shoes. She was right.

I was up until 2 a.m. trying to change the suit's colour by using black aerosol spray paint. The paint kept running and giving it an uneven colour even after I tried to dry it with Ilisha's hairdryer she loaned me ("You're one determined dude," she quipped). It took several coats of paint since the blue colour was so bright. Before I plopped into bed in exhaustion, I put the suit in a dark closet, in an insane off-chance it would absorb the blackness.

Sunday, June 26: Post-graduation prom. The day before began innocently enough with the bright sun shining through my bedroom window, dust flakes drifting lazily in the warm air. I saw a small bird on my windowsill, chirping the virtues of love. Chirping? Ugh—I fell asleep with my hearing aids on again.

Now I think of it, how little did the sparrow know that the owner of this windowsill was about to have a bad day. This was the day I shall call, "The Worst In My Life." Someday, I'll write a book about my ordeal.

I checked out the suit and sprayed another coat of black. 11:23 a.m. and still in my frog's pyjamas, I walked into the kitchen and saw a hysterical mother going to pieces on the phone. She had been on the phone all morning, calling different tuxedo rental places and wedding stores. She even went down the bottom of list to call YMCA offices, Salvation Army outlets and various clothing stores for poor people. Half of the city know what a horrible prom-goer I am.

"Yer aren't wearin' that blue thang," Mum scolded as she dialed another number. I mouthed a spoonful of Smurf-berry crunch cereal and said nothing. When I was on my third piece of toast, Dad came in with a grim expression and made Mum get off the phone.

"It's Mora—it's an emergency."

"Oh gawd, what timin'! What th' hell 'appened to Mora?"

When she uses the words "God" and "Hell" in one breath, it's not the time to ask her to buy more peanut butter.

"She's standing on roof of the Lakeshore General Hospital as we speak. Her husband left her last night and she's very distraught and suicidal," Dad explained. "She wants to only speak to you."

This means if Mora survives the jump, she would be an arm's length away from getting instant medical attention.

Mum grabbed her purse and as she opened the front door, she stopped and glared at me, "What are we gonna to do about yer prom suit?"

"Don't worry Mum, I found a black one," I twisted a kernel of a truth and out came a popcorn.

"What? I did all that callin' for nothin'?" she shouted.

I shrugged. And she was gone for the day with Dad.

I stayed home all day watching TV and eating chips alone, not feeling keen about tonight. With mounting nervousness, I took a good shower in the mid-afternoon and got dressed after Mrs. Tautog's lesson ("golf suit, golf suit, golf, golf, golf"). She again gave me the usual speech about informing people about my deafness—blah, blah, blah.

The paint on the suit was half-dry and it looked OK, except for a few thin spots of the original blue.

Hair in place, cologne dabbed, teeth brushed, I stood stiff and erect, my hands behind my back, in the front door entrance at precisely 6:15 p.m., a RCAF pilot awaiting a mission. The limo was due to arrive at about 6:35. I looked up and down the street and 6:35 passed by with no limo in sight. I waited a whole hour with increasing impatience, fidgeting with my green bow tie and wiping my sweaty palms on my legs. At the moment when I looked at my hands and saw that they had became spray-can black, the limo pulled up. Demoiselle, looking harried but beautiful, stepped out. I shoved my hands in my jacket pockets.

"Sorry Egg, we didn't know where you lived and we had to go back to my place so I could look through the recycling bin for your letter with your address on it." My letter was in the recycling bin? This tells me something new about Demoiselle: she's environmentally conscientious. I ducked into the white limo and met Demoiselle's friends and their dates seated inside. Demoiselle introduced me to each one but given my ineptitude in understanding spoken names, I had no idea who they were. I counted seven people in the limo: three girls and four guys. One guy sat next to Demoiselle and he scowled at me during the introductions. He looked suspiciously familiar—I recognized him from somewhere. Damn—he was the leather-jacketed guy I spied at the last dance!

All the way to the reception hall, everyone jabbered and laughed excitedly in the limo and I, clueless and left out, stared quietly out the window. Demoiselle didn't talk much either. A few minutes before we arrived, she tapped me on the elbow and slipped me a note. It read,

Sorry I not been in touch with you lately. My 83-year-old grandfather died last week of cirrhosis.

Missed you, Demoiselle XXOO

Then and there, the suit felt uncomfortable.

We arrived at the hotel and piled out of the limo and all seven of us walked up to the brightly lit entrance. I spied Jake standing on the other side of the street, hands in pockets and cap pulled low; he looked downcast watching people stream into the hall. Alfonsino, wearing cheesy movie-director sunglasses, swaggered by with a girl in a powder-blue frilly dress who looked as comfortable as a chipmunk in an eagle aviary. Demoiselle walked beside me and began to talk but the distant pounding of the music and car traffic behind me drowned out her voice. I did my usual act of bluffing and said, "Yes, yes" and "Really?" when it felt appropriate. She soon clammed up and her face became tense, lips squeezing shut firmly. I glanced nervously at her from the corner of my eyes and she stopped on her tracks. She crossed her arms and her eyes bore into mine. This is not good, I thought to myself. She mumbled something that sounded like a question.

Rather than shoot a "Yes," I decided to play it safe and asked, "Huh, say again?"

She became tense, her eyes narrowing.

"Did you hear anything what I just said?" she yelled, her face contorting.

I crumpled. "No," I mumbled meekly, "I'm hearing impaired."

"You lied to me!" She screamed. It's surprising how much I can understand speech when someone is pissed off. "Why didn't you tell me? You go on pretending you are hearing, telling all those lies! You're not doing yourself a favour! A relationship is based on honesty, Egg—" her voice went down several decibels, tears streamed down her cheeks.

She straightened up, smoothed out her dress and calmly mouthed, "I think we should stop seeing each other."

I stood there wordless and numb, staring in her teary eyes, my mind blank. It was silent and the cool night air ruffled my hair. I was distinctly aware of a good crowd of people assembling around us.

"I've something to show you, Egg," she spoke up as she reached back and took something out of her hair. She dangled the object in front of my face and said, "What do you make of this?"

My jaw dropped in utter shock and my mind snapped. I stared at the object in disbelief. I've known this object all my life.

It was a hearing aid.

She's hearing impaired! All this time, she was hearing impaired like me and everything could've been different between us. In terms of missed chances, I didn't even hit a barn door. The rest of the night were multi-coloured bits and pieces of hazy memories bobbing to the surface of my consciousness: her leaving me standing on the hall steps, my tears, the pouring rain, the lost wanderings in the slick black streets, the long taxi ride back home by a kind Jamaican in dreadlocks and lastly, getting into bed in my paint-streaked wet tux.

I stayed in bed all day, wallowing in quiet desperation and swimming in deep depression. On my occasional trips to the bathroom, low death noises rumbled from my throat as I dragged my heavy and sluggish feet across the tiles. It was because my heart, being encased in cement, had sunk to the bottom of my feet. I was still wearing my smeared tux. I'm lying in the dark, deep bowels of despondency, my body numb and inert, all my feelings have receded into the heavy, dank pits of my soul. Once-bright colours of my room ceased to be, sounds are muffled and distant and sensations are foreign and emotionless.

At 3:15 p.m., I summoned enough strength to change into my T-shirt and shorts. I told my whole family about last night at suppertime, with updated background information for Dad and Ilisha.

Each reacted differently. Mum put her arms around me and said, "There are plenty o' birds in the air."

Dad pursed his lips and said, "Hmmm" as if he was looking at a car engine making strange noises.

Ilisha didn't console me much, except to pat on my back. "Hey Egg, been there too. Hurts eh? You, she's just as bad as you, she should've told you that she was hearing impaired in the first place." She had a good point.

Thinking back, I should've seen the signs that she was hearing impaired: her not turning around when I called her name in the movie theatre, her long hair covering her ears (never seen her hair in a ponytail) and her misunderstanding a few questions. I now understood why she talked so much at the last dance: she took control of the conversation and talked a mile a minute rather than to listen.

I was too laconic to eat and did little today. Even the best WWII pilots spent time in deep funks like I did. I sat in the front porch ruminating about last night, dully watching cars pass by. The nightmarish scene replayed itself repeatedly in my mind: "...stop seeing each other...stop seeing each other..." Images of Demoiselle's hearing aid seared my brain. I kicked myself with "What if" questions and thoughts that I should've, could've and would've done this or that. Damn, I wish I could turn the clock back and avoid doing all those stupid back flips to keep Demoiselle in the dark about my hearing impairment. Ilisha was right—why she didn't tell me about her own deafness? What if I was forthcoming, would've it had made a difference last night? If I was serious about a long-term commitment, how could've I kept up the charade? She would've found out sooner or later. Unfortunately in my case, it was sooner.

Monday, June 27: I again slept for the better part of the morning. Only Mum prevented me from sleeping past 11:45 a.m. She put her face close to my dazed eyes and slowly mouthed, "Get up, Egg, today is the first day for the fish in the sea." This didn't help me. There was one fish I cared about and she's gone, swimming away into the depths with a shark in a leather jacket. Who was he anyway?

I went back to bed after a breakfast of dried toast and woke up at 1:35. With half-closed eyes, I dully gazed at my calendar above my desk and spied a scribble on today's date.

Hmm, I thought. I dragged myself to the desk and I looked at it closely. It read, "Aviation college entrance interview at 2:00." *Tabernac!* My eyes popped wide open and my hair did an impression of Buckwheat. The next several minutes was a blur of slapping on good clothing, scrubbing my teeth, pressing down my hair, begging Ilisha to drive me to the interview and whipping our way on Lakeshore road. Already 15 minutes late, I arrived at a large 18th century grey stone building and spent the next 15 minutes scrambling around in the maze of ancient halls, trying to find the damn room.

Sweat dripping from my forehead, clothes askew, hair like a mess of fishing string, I found a large ancient door with a small note that read, "Aviation interview chamber" and opened it. I stepped into a cavernous room and a panel of five uptight-looking military people sat impatiently behind a cheap table in the centre of this stately room. It had 50-foot high ceilings and opulent wood-panelled walls that hung several oil paintings of steely-eyed dignitaries scowling down at minions passing beneath. I gulped and sat on the lone metallic chair that was a good 30 feet away from the table.

"You're late," one man in an admiral uniform boomed. "We have five minutes left."

A grey-haired lady next to him began the interview with a question. Her voice was so soft, so distant and so incomprehensible.

"Pardon me?"

She sighed and said the same utterance with the same whispered tone.

"Sorry, can you speak louder please? I'm hearing impaired."

The woman stopped. All five panelists frowned simultaneously and they looked at each other. My cheeks felt hot. I began to fidget as I watched the important heads turn this way and that and speak in hushed tones. They stopped and five heads turned to me. My chair felt wet. The admiral glowered at me sternly.

"You can't fly. You are hearing impaired. All cadets are required to have excellent hearing as well as excellent health and sight." I felt a resounding pop in my mind and my stomach plummeted to the earth's core. I barely heard the admiral's ensuing explanation on the importance of clear communication between the ground control and pilots and other important-sounding babble. It didn't matter. My dream had already crashed and burned.

I took a slow bus home in ever-deepening depths of depression. First, Demoiselle dumps me because I was hiding my hearing impairment and my life-long dream was shot out of the sky because I admitted it. This society is giving me mixed messages.

At home, I took down all my airplane posters in my bedroom and shoved all the models away in the closet. Only the newly made Avro Arrow model hangs forlornly from the empty ceiling. My walls are bare except for a few girlie pictures. I plodded into our damp, dingy basement and watched TV vacantly and changed the channel whenever I saw a plane or a girl resembling Demoiselle but I couldn't turn off those images in my mind.

Mum caught me watching a three-hour documentary on the leather shoe industry and I told her what happened. Tears welling up, she said, "Oh Egbert, what are you goin' to do? How come you didn't know you needed perfect hearin' to be a pilot?"

All my knowledge of aspects flying, I had only focused on specs, the physics of flying and war combat stories and ignored the boring topics such as air traffic control and radio communication. Damn.

Dad's way of lifting my mood was to advise me "to learn from your mistakes. Look back at your experience and ask yourself, 'What did I learn from this?' Only then you will benefit from a negative experience."

Tuesday, June 28: I woke up this early afternoon with orange fuzzy visions and high-pitch cat noises in my ears. I was still in the basement, hearing aids on, face down on the orange shag carpet and the TV on to lunch cartoons. I rolled over to my back and stared at the ceiling. I thought about my hearing impairment—who am I? What am I doing here? What am I going to do? Physiologically, my missing a few microscopic cochlear hair cells doesn't make me any more different from a hearing person missing a finger, but I'm learning it makes one hell of a difference.

Mum discovered me mumbling at the ceiling and forced me to drag my inert body and vacant mind upstairs to take me shopping and have lunch in effort to cheer me up. Going to the shopping centre made it worse. I saw three planes in the air and many couples were walking about hand-in-hand. All I could do is to watch and pine for what could've been. What truly depressed me was seeing lonely old men scratching lotto tickets, pitifully hoping for a dream underneath their fingernails and never winning. The only bright spot today was seeing Molly. Mum and I had separated and I was passing by the music store and there I spied her, looking gorgeous as ever with her long wavy black hair down her bare shoulders, riffling through tape cassettes. She was with a blond girl, the same one she sat with on the day I saw them smoking on the bus in January. With Demoiselle gone and having nothing to lose, I might as well try to bag Molly—I made a beeline for the store and parked to the next row, pretending to be interested the Jimi Hendrix collection. I watched her from the corner of my eyes, hoping to catch her attention. I wanted to play it cool, as if this was an accidental bumping into each other kind of thing. She glanced around; her eyes passing over me and deftly put a Kiss cassette in her purse. She continued to browse a few more seconds and nodded to the blond girl before walking casually out of the store. She stole the cassette! Not only she illegally smokes on the bus, runs around with older guys, drives as if she needs training wheels, she shoplifts! Could I love a girl like her? What am I saying? Is she my "backup" plan?

At nine o'clock this evening, my parents herded Ilisha and me into the living room for a "family meeting." They made a shocking announcement that will change my life forever, change the way I view our family and change the foundations of who I am.

Dad's exact words were, "We have something important to tell you both. You two have an older sibling, a brother. We felt it was optimal time to inform you because he's coming home in a few weeks."

Ilisha and I sat there for a few moments, numb and mouths agape. Our barrage of questions came and with Dad's patient answers, the full picture emerged. He's hearing impaired! Same as me! Out of all the details about his history, this was most exciting detail about him. His name is Patrick and in 1960, he was placed at the Huchen Mental Institute when he was three years old because he was misdiagnosed as autistic.

"Children with this rare condition," Dad explained, "are usually mute. Not until he was five years old, the doctors learned that he wasn't autistic, but deaf." After a series of IQ tests designed for hearing children that were administered by examiners with no knowledge of deafness, Patrick was diagnosed as being "mentally retarded."

"Tests back then were awful, they had poor cultural biases." Patrick's diagnosis too proved to be wrong several years later.

Right before he was to be released as a teen, he was again mistakenly diagnosed, this time as having borderline personality disorder. This was a diagnosis was formed after a five-minute assessment by an aging psychiatrist with no skills in communicating with the deaf. This kept Patrick in the hospital for another five years. By the time the mistake was discovered, he had developed other supposed "behavioural problems" such as violent anger outbursts which kept him in the hospital until recently. I don't blame him.

Hospital policy doesn't normally allow psychiatrists to work with their own family members but my father learned of his history and fought to have Patrick's case transferred to him two years ago. Since Patrick has never lived outside the institution, Dad taught him independent life-skills and was successful enough to permit him to be released and go home.

"Patrick doesn't talk but communicates using manual language." Dad made an effort to learn American Sign Language (ASL for short) and taught this to Patrick and he picked it up with joy and speed.

"When he was a toddler, we initially tried to teach him to speak but as soon as we found that he didn't have the aptitude, we switched to teaching him ASL. He learned and used it for a few years. When he was transferred another hospital, no one communicated with him and he lost the language. No one kept me informed of his file because of confidentiality regulations. When he was transferred back to my hospital, I had to re-teach him ASL and he picked it up fast because he already had the language rules set in his brain. It proved to be better for him in the end."

Dad said he's a bright engaging man with a good sense of humour and all preconceived notions about him were wrong.

"Why did you keep this a secret?" Ilisha spoke for both of us.

"It was something we should not have done. I guess it was a sense of shame—having a family member with a mental illness and me being a psychiatrist," Dad said ruefully. "I should've known better. He was never mentally ill to begin with and we all lost many years being out of touch. We should focus on the present, not dwell on the 'shoulds' or 'could'ves' and make each day forward count." Maybe he was talking about me as well.

We'll be visiting him tomorrow and Dad will act as a translator for him and us. Wow! This means I can put aside suicidal thoughts of becoming a target sheet replacement boy in a shooting club for twelve-year-old juvenile delinquents with ADHD.

Before heading to bed, Dad came to me while I was watching the Montreal Expos baseball game alone downstairs and sat facing me.

"When we see Patrick tomorrow, I know it will be a significant event for you. One word of advice: don't call him 'hearing impaired.'"

I frowned quizzically.

"He prefers to be called 'Deaf.' Signing deaf people label themselves as 'Deaf' with a big 'D' because it's a cultural name, like 'Irishman' with a big 'I'. People who are deaf but have speech usually call themselves 'hearing impaired' as you do or 'deaf' with a small 'd'. If you call him hearing impaired, it will deny his culturally identity."

Hmmm. Sounds interesting. I want to learn more about this "Deaf."

Wednesday, June 29: I scarcely slept last night. The prom fiasco and crushed dreams of flying were put in the back burner and meeting my newfound older brother was in the front burner in my mind. What does he look like? How will he react to us? How can talk to him in ASL if I don't know the language?

We left home in the morning to take an hour-long drive into the country. The hospital was out of the way, because, as Dad explained, "People don't want 'loony bins' in their neighbourhood. 'Out of sight, out of mind' is what they want."

The hospital was a huge stately turn-of-the century building nestled upon large tracts of rolling lawns and small forests. A few patients in blue hospital gowns wandered freely on the grass. We entered through a large time-worn wood door.

After passing through a series of locked doorways and security checkpoints, we arrived in a large lounge where we saw more patients calmly milling about. It wasn't a chaotic scene as I thought it would be—no crazy-looking people with unruly hair screaming, banging their heads against the walls, or cowering in dark corners in fear of being followed by a tuba. One girl resembled Demoiselle and I had to turn away as her voice echoed in my mind, "...stop seeing each other...stop seeing each other." In the hallway I passed by an old woman with a large button on her gown that read, "Kiss me twice, I have multiple personalities."

We arrived at Patrick's door, and entering a double-occupancy room, we saw, a fat, unshaven, beef of a man with sun burnt hair, ruddy cheeks, deep leathery skin sitting up in bed. He had on a large cowboy hat, a toothpick in mouth and two spiteful black eyes. A pack of cigarettes was on his night table next to several greasy pork rinds and a recent issue of the TV Times. He probably believes that health is the slowest possible rate at which one can die.

"Whatcha looking at, boy?" in a deep voice that rattled my sternum. I gulped. My brother can talk!

Dad went around the bed and pulled aside the curtain next to the greasy man to reveal a tall lanky blond man sitting in a chair next to the bed, reading. He put down the novel, looked up and beamed at us.

Dad motioned to the blond man in bed. "This is Patrick." Whew, this one was less threatening. Mum strode up to him and hugged him. Dad faced him and his hands made signs in the air and introduced him to Ilisha and me. Patrick looked at us and grinned. He stood up and hugged us. Ilisha cried softly—tears of joy or agony of having another deaf brother? He was especially happy to meet me. We stood around and talked to him with wavering voices for a short while and Dad interpreted everything. He's looking forward to going home in a few weeks and getting to know the family he never had.

"Sorry about your name," he signed to me. "Mom and Dad should've named me 'Ham'. We would've had fun introducing ourselves as 'Ham and Eggs.'" We all laughed at that one.

Overall, Patrick looks and acts normal. When he signs, his hand movements are so strange and foreign but beautiful to watch at the same time. On the way home, Dad explained how he taught Patrick to read and write by combining ASL, pictures and written English words. He gave him many books to read to bide his time in the hospital. My brother is exceedingly intelligent, scoring a 133 on an I.Q. test adapted for the Deaf.

"He's within the very superior intelligence range," Dad said with a hint of pride. He could do my homework for me.

I was in the kitchen eating my pre-bed snack when Ilisha came to me with a newspaper clipping from the Montreal Star. "Hey bro, read this." It was an article about a Deaf man who flies a Cessna 207 airplane as a hobby. He's permitted to fly as long as he has a hearing co-pilot with him.

"See, Egg," pointing to the picture of the man. "You can still fly." I smiled.

Thursday, June 30: Being alone with my mum is getting on my nerves. She dropped broad hints that I should be out looking for a summer job.

"You know the story of the grasshopper and the ant...," she trailed off.

No, I don't, I thought and continued to read the newspaper. Jeez, I just finished school a few days ago. I'm not ready for the rat race yet. Besides, I'm still suffering from the two recent traumas: The Worst Day Of My Life and The Crash and Burn Of My Twin-engine Dream.

An hour later: "I'm not 'aving you sit around 'n read the damn newspaper—go to th' job centre!" she shrilled. I slowly changed out of my frog pyjamas and took the bus to the shopping centre. The job centre can wait as long I'm out of Mum's hair.

I went to the hobby store and while looking at the Curtiss P-40 Warhawk model, I felt a hand softly tap my shoulder. It was Molly! "Hi cutie, I see you like planes?" I nodded, "Y-y-y- yeah." My mood went up a notch.

"I'll buy that for you," she said as she took the box from my hands, her fingers brushing against mine. We went to the counter with my head lighter than air and she paid with her credit card. I thanked her as we strode out the store. We walked around and she talked and I nodded along, a lovesick dog. We passed by Alfonsino swaggering by in a black muscle T-shirt (without the muscle). He gave me a thumbs-up gesture and mouthed, "Awesome, man, go for it."

When Molly said something, she faced me each time and I was able to understand most of what she said. No street cleaning machines this time. I forgot all about Demoiselle and the Aviation academy rejection; Molly will be the salve to sooth the pain of my two lost loves.

"Come with me, I need your opinion," she put her hands into mine and led me in to a bikini store. I spaced out. She browsed through the bathing suit rack, picked a few items and walked towards the back. She turned around to face me and motioned me to a plush chair. "Sit here and tell me what you think." She disappeared into the changing room and appeared a few minutes later, wearing nothing but a blue string bikini and high heels! "Eep!" I squeaked. She seductively turned around to give me a look of her backside. Red-faced, I gave her thumbs up. She tried two other bathing suits but both were not as sexy as the first one.

"You adore the blue one right, Eggie? You don't think it shows too much?" I shook my head and said, "It's a nice colour." Man! What a dorky answer!

After Molly changed back to her jeans and low-cut halter-top, she rested her hand on my lap and leaned over me while I was still sitting in the chair. I gawped at her boobs hanging down from under her shirt a foot away as she whispered something in my ear. From the corner of my eyes, I saw her slip the blue bikini in my airplane model bag. She stood up and said in my face, "Let's go have a coffee together, cutie-pie," and, arm in mine, she led me out the store with me carrying the bag with the contraband. My hypnotized body was in Molly's control. My heart was pounding and my knees were jelly—she was making me shoplift! A few steps out of the store, a heavy hairy hand clapped on my shoulder. I slowly turned to see the owner of the hand—the security guard! He said something in French while gesturing to my bag. "Uh uh, je-je-je ne comprende pas." I stammered.

"Eh, eh, me look in sac," he said firmly, with a heavy French accent. People stopped strolling to stand and stare at us. I gave him the bag with trembling hands. He opened the bag, looked at me with a stern expression and talked into his walkie-talkie. I glanced to the left of me and—damn—Molly was gone!

"Viens," he motioned me into the store and led me to a small office in the back, his hand gripping my elbow, the same one Molly was holding so gently moments earlier.

I sat in the office and, can you believe it—I began to cry! RCAF POWs would never cry when captured by the enemy! An old woman came in and sat across from me with the security guard blocking the door so I wouldn't get any rash ideas of escaping. I assumed the old bag was the manager of the store.

"You're in big trouble, young man. You did something seriously illegal." I bawled. She asked for my ID card and I, sniffling, showed the only card I had—my Canterbury ID card. She demanded my phone number and called home. I was sick to my stomach, my back was sweaty and hands were shaking.

"Your mother is coming to pick you up." She went on a long explanation that, while she won't call the police and charge me with shoplifting this time, what I did was illegal, I could've had a record, other countries would've chopped off my hand, blah, blah, blah. I sat there, her words washing over my sniffles and sobs. Punishment from my parents will be dire enough. A loud knock on the door interrupted the manager's diatribe. My parents! The security guard opened the door and in walked was...my sister! Not only that, she was wearing Mum's coat and her reading glasses.

"Egbert Flounder! What's wrong with you?" she glared at me. She proceeded to yell at me, she was disappointed in me, what I did was wrong, that I must go to Church and pray every day for my sins and so on. She took a deep breath and turned to the manager. "I do apologise for my son's awful behaviour. Don't you worry, my husband and I'll punish him severely." She grabbed my arm and yanked me out of the office. I was shocked—I'd never seen her so violent. She stormed out the shopping centre with me straggling behind her. We sat into her Honda and she shocked me again—she hugged me!

"Hey Egg, sorry for yelling at you back there, I had to convince the lady. Why did you do that for?" I was honest, told her the story of how Molly led me astray.

"Oh, I knew you couldn't have done this on your own – why would you steal a bikini?" I wiped away a tear and she looked at me with pity. "And don't worry bro, I won't tell Mum and Dad." I breathed a deep sigh of relief and my shaking stopped. I saw my sister in a different light today.

After being burned by Molly and my heart and my brain working on different shifts, I called Demoiselle on my own tonight. I dialed and a male voice answered. It didn't sound like the craggy, grumpy voice of her father, but a suspicious younger voice.

"H-hello, may I speak to Demoiselle?" The receiver crackled as the guy mumbled something and the phone fell silent. After a long pause, a female voice came on the phone. It was Demoiselle! My heart began to pound and my throat dried up.

"Hi Demoiselle, this is Egg."

Demoiselle garbled something.

"Sorry, can you repeat please?"

The same garble again but louder.

Mum appeared nearby. "She says she's not Demoiselle. It's her sister." This was strange. Demoiselle has the exact same voice.

"Well, can I speak to Demoiselle please?"

"Do you have a TTY?" Mum mouthed.

"No—what's a TTY?"

The line went dead and I felt like crap. Why the hell did I do a stupid stunt like this? What was I thinking?

I felt much, much worse after. As I was about to succumb to the comfortably numb embrace of dark despair, I realized something—I had been talking to Demoiselle's hearing sister all this time! Demoiselle had been standing by and dictating to her sister. Damn! Who is the bigger faker now?

July

Friday, July 1ˢᵗ: Canada day. I woke up thinking about Demoiselle and I, enraged, bitter and infuriated, punched my pillow over and over again. Mum came in and saw me with tears in my eyes. "Uh, I fell and hurt my hand," I lied.

"Never mind yer girl, Egg. Get dressed, we're gonna see your brother afta breakfast." How did she know?

On the way to the Huchen Mental Institute to visit Patrick, Mum asked me if I wanted a TTY and other devices for the Deaf.

"What's a TTY?"

"It's a special thang for Deaf folks like ya, Egg. It means Teletypewriter. It's a keyboard with this screen 'n ya can put the phone on top 'n type what you wanna to say. The other person must have th' same thing to read the message 'n type back."

"What if I wanted to call a hearing person who doesn't have one?" I asked, my mind racing of nights of calling for pizzas, new plane models and phone sex lines.

"Ya can call a 'earing person by first callin' a special relay operator who would type out what th' other person says and then readin' out loud what you type."

Forget sex phone lines. Grandmotherly relay operators wouldn't appreciate listening and transcribing such smutty calls. Heavy breathing would be difficult to convey on the TTY thing.

Other than that, it sounds good to me. I can't rely on Mum forever to stand by and interpret my calls. She might someday get laryngitis.

Seeing my interest, Mum said, "I'll call 'round and get ya one. Patrick is gonna need it too. We can get other stuff that'll help both of ya."

We arrived at the hospital and saw Dad briefly on his rounds, but he was too busy with a patient to come with us to visit our newest family member. Mum and I talked to Patrick for about a half-hour. She knows a few signs but we communicated mainly by writing notes. It was inconvenient and took longer but I found Patrick to be incredibly patient throughout. I learned a few signs myself, it's so new and fascinating, a seed of excitement is growing inside me.

Driving out the parking lot, Mum was listening the radio and laughed. She said the hospital has its own radio show broadcasting once a week and features two actual patients. Lars and Gars presented a one-hour segment called "The Madcap Minute" which, according to Mum, entirely consisted of Lars giggling uncontrollably and Gars reminding him that he's on air.

After supper, Mum, Dad, Ilisha and I went to the Mackenzie park for the Canada Day celebrations. Under the setting sun, we walked among the crowds, listened to the band, ate hot dogs and watched the fireworks. A twinge of pain and the sense of loss still hits me when I see a plane in the sky or an amorous couple walking by. A few times, I thought I saw Demoiselle's face in the crowd, only to get mixed feelings.

Another face that gave me mixed feelings was Molly's. While I was waiting in line by myself for a free hot dog, I saw Molly walk by. When she saw me, I glared at her and turned my back to her. She stepped into my view and her eyes locked into mine. I tore myself away from her hypnotic eyes and looked out to the lake. She put her hands on my shoulders and gently turned me around. She stood close to me, her eyes filled with sorrow and took my hands, clasping them in front of her cleavage.

"I'm so sorry, Eggie. I feel terrible."

"You walked away and I got into trouble!"

"I was scared, honest, I didn't mean to do that, believe me."

I stood firmly there, mouth tightly closed, but I secretly enjoyed her attention and begging.

"Please forgive me, I'm so sorry," her red lips forming the word "Sorry" clearly.

I, a stupid goof overruled by my southern regions, said, "It's ok, forget it."

"Honestly?" she exclaimed, her eyes widening.

"Yes, it's ok. No problem." She jumped forward and gave me a hug. I felt her chest pressing against mine.

"Thank you, you're such a darling. Can you bring me the bikini tomorrow?"

Huh? I gave her a blank look. "Sorry, the store took it back before I was questioned by the owner."

An awkward pause filled her face. "Too bad. Bye." She walked off with her blond friend.

Ilisha rushed up to me, "Who was that—Demoiselle?"

"No, the girl who made me shoplift." My sister strode right up to her and gave her an earful. I couldn't make out the words because they were a good 50 paces away, but man, she absolutely reamed her. Molly flipped her hair and tried to look cool answering Ilisha's rants with short phrases. Ilisha eventually stopped and huffed past me. Molly glanced at me over her shoulder and ambled away into the crowd.

Can you believe this? My hands were *this* close to her breasts!

Saturday, July 2: Today was my last lesson with Mrs. Tautog. I was surprisingly but briefly sad. Who will help me say "Irene" and "Virgina" without sounding as if I have a potty mouth?

At the end of our session, Mrs. Tautog said, "You are on your own, if you need more lessons, you can call me but your parents will have to pay my tutorial fees. The government only cover the services to high school students," she explained. "I'm proud of you, your speech is much better anyway." I beamed. My parents thanked her and gave her a small gift before she left.

Mum drove me to the disabilities government office to get my TTY and other equipment. A nice pudgy woman looked at my audiogram from Dr. Albacore to make sure that I qualified for the free devices and processed my order. She gave me a box full of devices for Patrick and me.

To emphasize my hearing impairment, I made sure I said, "Pardon?" and "Say again, please." She spoke clear as a bell and I didn't want her to think I was malingering.

"You poor hearing impaired people need all the help you need," she said before we left.

We installed everything at home and tested them. They're all amazing! On each floor, there's a light that will flash when the phone rings or the doorbell sounds. I can tell if someone is at the door from anywhere around the house. No more waiting near the front door for a damn 'fridge repairman!

I put the bed-shaker under my mattress and plugged it to a timer along with my bedside light. At a preset time, I will be shaken awake by the bed shaker and have 200-watt light bulb scorching my face every bloody morning. Mum was especially happy with this, not having to wake me up and duck if I throw a punch in my sleep.

We tested the flashing smoke detector by pushing the test button and is it ever bright! "Great," I thought. "The whole neighbourhood will see whenever Dad burns dinner."

Mum showed me how to use the TTY and we called Grandma via relay service and for the first time, I no longer need to depend on Mum to translate. It even prints conversations in case I forget to write down important information.

The best device is the closed-captioned decoder for the TV. It shows spoken words on the bottom of the screen similar to English subtitles in foreign-language films. I now understand everything they say on TV!

This is making me wonder: who am I now? The hearing impaired ex-RCAF wanna-be with floppy ears or a Deaf teen learning to sign and no longer needing Mum to translate or wake me up?

I feel lighter today—getting the assistive devices and the discovery of my new Deaf older brother distanced me from my pain. But a dark cloud: what am I going to do after high school? I was so hung up on flying I've no idea of what else I could do. Dad encouraged me to pursue something related to writing and added that a fashion model changing room attendant is "not a realistic career option."

Sunday, July 3: We went to the Huchen Institute to visit Patrick. We found him playing chess with a man with multiple personality disorder and beating him badly. I think each personality had his own strategy.

I asked Dad, "If a patient with seven personalities were to threaten suicide, does it become a hostage situation?"

Patrick finished the game quickly and we all went outside to take a nice summer's day stroll in the hospital gardens. We mainly talked about his preparation to go home next week and his future plans. He wants to go to Gallaudet University to get his bachelor's degree and continue there to study for his master's degree in teaching. Dad interpreted the whole conversation. Patrick taught me a signs for "boy," "girl,", "sister", "brother," "school" and "learn." They were easy and a few were logical. The sign for "learn," for instance, was a movement of picking up something from the palm of one hand and moving it to your forehead as if to pick up knowledge from a book and putting in it your head. He gave me a sheet with the alphabet in ASL and showed me how to do each letter. "Practise spelling," he signed in encouragement.

Back at the hospital, while Dad and Patrick were deep in signed conversation, I wandered around the room and saw the greasy Texan sleeping behind the curtain. On the wall next to him was a handwritten piece of paper. It read:

- If the toothbrush is wet, you've just brushed your teeth.
- If you're wearing one brown shoe and one black shoe, you have a pair like it in the closet.
- Your wallet is in the other pants.
- How to live to be 100: live for 99 years and be very careful for one year.

I watched TV all night long with the captions, even the crappy shows like the 2-hour special, "Stamp collecting for the lactose-intolerant." Even a few commercials were captioned!

I memorized the signed alphabet before going to sleep and got them all down to pat even the tricky letters 'k', 'p'.

Monday, July 4: Mum dragged me out of bed at 7 a.m. and mouthed into my muzzy face, "go 'n git a job, no more sleepin', sittin' around and doin' nothin'."

I grudgingly ate my C-3PO cereal and pedalled over to the employment bureau. While walking across the parking lot, I saw Jake with his father; he has the same face but was smaller bodied. They were standing in between cars and his father was yelling at him. Jake shouted something back and the father smacked him across the face several times, grabbed his shirt and shoved him into the pick-up truck. Jake looked frightened and I felt bad for him. Dad was right when he once explained, "Bullies are frequent victims of physical abuse at home. It's classic case of psychological displacement, the shifting an aggressive impulse to a less threatening target. A bully cannot hit his abuser, so he picks on someone smaller, or of less status, than him."

I hurried into the employment centre and found a good number of people crowded around the job bulletin boards craning their necks to read the postings. The job postings were typed on 3X4 cards tacked on a large bulletin board and included the job title, job description, starting salary and contact information. I had to eliminate many potential jobs that require a) fluent French, b) experience in doing so and so (how am I supposed to get the experience in the first place?) and c) use of the phone unless it's for a complaint department.

Alfonsino was there too, scanning the job board. "Hey man, seems all the gigolo jobs were taken. Guess I'll aim for the water boy job for the female volleyball team."

I found a few great-sounding jobs that involve working with planes such as cleaning, repairing and painting aircraft. If

I cannot fly them, at least I can still work with them. My summer began to look good. I cycled home, ate lunch and called the employers with my new TTY.

I dialed the relay operator and gave her the number to call. My first call was to AviationTech inc. even though they didn't know how to spell "ink."

A pause followed and the operator typed, "Explaining relay. Transferring call."

Another pause. "Explaining relay. Transferring call."

A yet another pause. "Explaining relay. Transferring call."

It must be one of those hot potato calls where no one wants to handle it and transfers the call to the next smoe.

"Hello, may I help you?" It must've been someone from the lowest end on the ladder of success that he was lying on the ground with his hands on the first rung.

I typed, "Hello sir, I'm responding to the wanted ad posted at the employment centre, can I make an appointment to fill out the application?" I typed this out with one finger. Damn— it's hard to find the keys.

"Uh, are you hearing impaired?"

"Yes, sir, " I responded.

Can you talk or do you use your hands?"

"I can speak quite clearly, sir. I don't know sign language yet."

"Are you blind?" This one bowled me over.

"No sir, only hearing impaired."

"Give me your phone number and I'll call you back."

I did but the operator told me he had already hung up. Crap. I soldiered on and asked the operator to dial number two on my priority list: Air Montreal. After the first "Explaining relay," the person hung up. I couldn't take any more psychological abuse so I stopped there. Besides, Ilisha was giving me dirty looks; she wanted to call a guy who, I think, is her new boyfriend.

After supper, I went into my room and practised my signed A-B-Cs and tried fingerspelling different words. I also reviewed all the signs Patrick showed me. It's strange, using the empty space in front me in meaningful way but I'm getting more comfortable with using my hands to "talk." I thought of something: if a signing Deaf person breaks both his hands, would he become "mute"?

Tuesday, July 5: I called more of those job wanted numbers I collected yesterday. Two of them told me that the position has been filled, one hung up and one tried to pick up the operator.

Guy (via operator): "Do want to have dinner at my place?"

Me: "Uh, no thanks."

Guy (now a jerk): "Hey cripple, I'm not talking to you, I'm trying to score a date with the operator."

The operator hung up this time.

The next call allowed me to come in to fill out the application. I cycled over to the Dorval Airport and met with the supervisor of a small airline company, a heavy-set man with a sweaty forehead and rolled up sleeves. His cheap blue tie bore the airline logo.

"Are you the hearing impaired boy who called before?"

"Yes, sir. I'm pleased to meet you."

"Do you have a stuffy nose?"

"No, sir, this is how I talk."

He shook his head as if he was shaking off excess sweat from his forehead and was kind enough to accommodate my hearing impairment. "Here! Fill out this application! Give it to the secretary!" he shouted. He was an observational man. He noticed I didn't have my great-grandfather's hearing apparatus—the ear funnel.

Looking at the application form, I noticed it wasn't for the airplane repairman assistant position I wanted but for a dishwasher job. The boss had already disappeared in his office, so I went ahead and filled out the form. I was at odds when it came to putting down our phone number. Should I put down the relay operator's number as well? Should I write a short explanation of how to call the operator to reach me? Should I simply put down our number, wait for them to call and tell them I'll call them right back via relay operator? Or should I let Mum handle the call and risk looking like a momma's boy?

I chose the least painful way and left the space blank. They can send me a letter to the address I supplied on the application. I handed the form to an old bat of a secretary who should be off teaching someone piano lessons on a hard bench. At least I left with a feeling of accomplishment.

Mum was less than impressed. "Only one? Ya can't stop there, Egg. Ya hafta fill out many, many applications to up yer odds of gettin' a job. Don't count yer chickens before they take flamingo lessons."

After supper, Mum, Dad and I visited Patrick; he was happy to see us. He taught me a few more signs: "hospital," "doctor," "family" and the four seasons and I showed him my new finger spelling skills. He says I'm a quick learner.

Ilisha invited a new boyfriend over for supper. "Babarosa" is a tweed-jacket wearing portly man with red hair and a full red beard. "He's at the Juliane University in pre-med, he wants to specialize in biochemistry of hormones. He's always curious about new things and people." Ilisha explained.

Given this curiosity and that he has never met a deaf person before, he paid attention to me for most of the evening with a perverse interest reserved for scientists examining legless sheep. He drilled me with hundreds of inane questions about my hearing impairment. The worst part was that each question had to be repeated twice because his bedraggled beard made it difficult for me to read his lips properly. I would only to catch a word or two, shoot a quizzical look at Mum and she'd repeat the question. His strong interest in me, interestingly enough, made Ilisha jealous. Given this, I didn't mind the scope of his interest, but this man's brain is only there to keep his head from caving in. Here is a snippet of our conversation:

"Do hearing impaired people read Braille?"

"Only in pornographic magazines."

"Are hearing impaired people mentally deficient?"

"Huh? I don't understand the question."

"How can you talk if you're hearing defective?"

"I'm not talking. My cat is a ventriloquist."

"What are those things in your ears?"

"Remote control transmitters. I can control and program appliances with it like the coffee machine. Cream?"

You get the gist. I couldn't get away with my absurd replies because Mum or Dad would invariably provide the correct answers. Too bad—he incredulously believed me the first time around.

Wednesday, July 6: I cycled back to the employment office and I ran into Alfonsino rushing out of the employment centre. "Hey my main man Egg!" He greeted me with a slap my back. "I found a job as a stripper! I start tomorrow! Can you believe it? All dem women will be shoving big wads of cash down my jock strap in no time!" At least he found his dream job.

I looked through more postings on the bulletin boards. I frowned when I saw two jobs that I've been told were "filled" were still posted. One of them was marked in red ink, "Urgent—immédiatement." Did they forget to take it down? Anyway, I found five new job postings. Three of them involved work with airplanes and two were so-so factory jobs with good pay.

I noticed something that turned my stomach: no TTY at the employment office. This is unfair. Hearing people can use the office's public phones but I have to call from home. They can snap up the jobs while I'm still on the road.

I spent the afternoon on my TTY and all didn't work out except one. One job required use of the walkie-talkie, two said, "Sorry, we don't hire hearing defective people." and another hung up. The one successful call was a person who talked to me as if I was a third person of the wrong gender. Example: "Ask her what jobs she has worked before." The supervisor set up an interview with me tomorrow at 2 pm. It was the job posting last on my list: an assembly-line job at a factory that produces music cassette cases. This will my very first job interview.

Mum gave me wise advice: "Dress well 'n fer God sakes, don't wear that ugly gawf suit. And, bring the CV I typed for ya last summer."

I was rummaging through my papers for my CV when found a picture of Tilapia. Man, that brought back memories. Tilapia was a girl I had a crush on in Grade 5. A sassy girl with long brown hair, freckles and a distinctive, but alluring gap between her two front teeth, Tilapia was a year older and, best of all, she was hearing impaired like me. We played cat's cradle at recess, passed flowery notes in the hall and talked face to face on the grass with the sun gleaming on her chestnut hair. She was my best friend. When Bobby Lenok pushed me onto the hard cement and called me a retard, Tilapia ran up and walloped him a good one in the chin. She got a week's detention for this and Bobby never touched me after this.

One sad rainy afternoon we sat on the St. Veronica's school steps on the last day school. She took my hands and told me that her family was moving back to Prince Edward Island. "Come with me, I want to show you something," she said in her deaf accent as she led me into the school's tool shed. Once inside, she turned to me, placed her hands softly on my shoulders and said, "Goodbye, Egg, I'll always remember you. Someday I'll come back to Montreal." She leaned forward and kissed me on the lips! She walked out of the tool shed and left me transfixed on the spot, speechless. I was only 11 years old! I couldn't understand what had happened on this day but I learned that girls were much more than giggles, flowery backpacks and friendship bracelets. It was the last time I saw her. For many years afterwards, I've searched in vain for a glimpse of Tilapia among departing schoolgirls, on packed buses and in downtown crowds. A few times, I had thought I saw her face, but it always turned out to be someone else. I gave this up a few years ago.

Thursday, July 7: I had my interview today. I dressed up in my best school clothes (suit and tie) and rode the bus there. Man, it was hot—35 degrees Celsius. I met the secretary at the front desk and she led me through a large warehouse filled with loud machines and sweating workers to the boss's office in the back. I spied Alfonsino working in the corner and yes, he was working as a stripper all right—stripping paint off old school desks. He looked miserable.

The secretary introduced me to Mr. Sockeye. He was a small wiry man with a nervous facial tic and throughout the interview he grimaced, fidgeted and chain-smoked. He never once looked at me straight in the eye; his eyes roamed everywhere around the office except at me. This didn't make it any easier for the poor sap sitting across from him.

I was sweating, my tie was choking me and the cigarette smoke was burning my eyes, all of which degraded my lip-reading skills. At the start of the interview, he had to repeat each question, which he did with a deep sigh of impatience. Deciding not to bother him with any more requests to repeat, I threw my answers at him with wild abandon. I guess I was hoping at least one would hit the target. Don't blame me—I was oxygen-deprived at the time.

He soon stopped questioning me and talked non-stop in a quick clip in French, his hands fiddling with his tie, the coin paperweight and his hair. He talked. And talked. And talked. I squinted through a watery blur of cigarette smoke, moving lips and a bobbing head of greasy hair. My head swam in a dizzy stream of nonsense blather and my stomach rowed frantically against a whirlpool of bile. I wobbled on my feet, grabbed the edge of his desk and barfed at the general whereabouts of his garbage pail. It was on the other side of the desk.

I remember him stopping dead, his mouth open, cigarette dangling from his lower lip. I bolted out of his office and ran through the clanking machines and took the bus home with a literally and figuratively bad taste in my mouth. My first interview and I ralphed my macaroni and cheese dinner on his carpet.

Mum asked me how my interview went and I was vague, saying, "I made a colourful lasting impression."

Still feeling nauseous, I spent the rest of the evening in bed, reading comic books and practised finger spelling the characters' names.

Saturday, July 9: I felt better this morning and went to the shopping centre and received the best surprise of my short miserable life! I was eating poutine in the food court when I noticed a group of signing Deaf people a few tables from me. I couldn't take my eyes off them, entranced by their fluid body movements, animated hands and rubber facial expressions. I caught an odd sign or two that I knew. A girl glanced in my direction and looked right at me. Getting hot under my collar, I looked down and focused on eating my French fries. From the corner of my eyes, I saw her get up and walk over. Oh crap, she will tell me off for staring at them, I thought.

I felt a soft tap on my back. I looked up at this beautiful girl and she said, "Egbert? Is that you?"

I gaped—Tilapia! My elementary school sweetheart! I still recognized her even though I had not seen her since grade 5. My heart began to pound as fresh memories of her kissing me six years ago came rushing back again. What a coincidence—I find her grade 6 picture yesterday and see her in person today, looking five years older.

I blurted, "Hi, Tilapia, great to see you again!"

"Come with me, bring your food," she beckoned. She still has the slight "deaf" accent like mine.

She brought me over to her friends' table and introduced me. Even though I'm not fluent in sign language, they were patient enough to mouth certain words for me and use gestures. With the few signs I knew, I told them I have a signing Deaf brother and they were impressed.

The whole time I was with them, I felt awkward but happy to be with those who have experienced the same frustrations, pain and misfortunes in a hearing world. But, the difference lies in the fact that I can talk and they can't or choose not to. The best part of this afternoon's encounter was when Tilapia asked me for my phone number and gave me hers without my asking. "I'll call you soon with my TTY," she said before we separated.

Yes! The ashes have fallen from my burnt relationship with Demoiselle and the Phoenix may rise again soon.

More evidence that people in the outside world aren't as bright as I thought: Babarosa ate supper with us again. If I were stranded on an island and had a choice of a having an AM radio (a real gibberish box to me) or Babarosa, I'd pick the radio. It would be easier to write, "Rescue me," notes on the radio. More questions from the sub-terrestrial vault of stupidity:

"You think well for a hearing impaired person. Are the rest of your people hearing impaired and dumb?"

"Only to those hearing folks who turn a deaf ear."

"How do hearing impaired people make babies?"

"The same way you do, sir."

"You have a hearing defect, is there anything else you have that is defective?"

"I do occasionally get the urge to floss my teeth on the bus."

I can't take this moron and his line of questioning anymore. What bothers me the most is his use of the term, "Hearing defect" because it implies that I'm "defective," as if my Mum could've exchanged me for jumper cables. We don't refer to people without hands as "Hand-defective", or blind people as "Eye defective." How come he never asked me about my interest in being a pilot, about school, or my future plans? He chose to focus on those "defective" ears I have on each side of my head.

Sunday, July 10: Guess who came to my door this afternoon? Luderick! His head was shaved and he was wearing the traditional Freebob grab: sunglasses, black suit, white shirt and a solid black tie. "Hey Egg!" he exclaimed. "Glad to see ya!" We went into the kitchen and talked. The Freebobs are in Montreal to do their recruitment campaign and he snuck away to see me. He says he's happy with his new friends; they listen to him seriously without treating him like a strange duck. He even has a new girlfriend who accepts his strange ideas, his being a secret cross-dresser and all.

"I feel at home, Egg—everyone likes me!" He says his mom has been begging him to come back and prays for him every night at his bedroom door.

"Mom never accepted me for who I am, she was always trying to suck me into her religion, taking me to church and stuff." When he walked out, I watched him stroll down the sunny side of the street with a new step until he disappeared around the corner. A tear welled up to my eyes and I smiled to myself.

Anyway, Dad announced that Patrick officially obtained his discharge papers from the hospital and he'll be coming home tomorrow afternoon. Mum worked all day converting the basement room into a more suitable room. I helped her paint.

At suppertime, Mum complained she was pestered by three "annoying calls that sounded like a fax machine."

"I hadda run up 'n down the stairs each time the phone rang. I ran 'round like a chicken wi' his head shaved."

"Mum, it should be 'a chicken with his head cut off,'" I corrected her.

"If yer head was shaved, you'd be runnin' around a lot faster, instead of bumpin' into things without a head, wouldn't you?"

Aerodynamically speaking, she had a point.

Ilisha said Barborosa was impressed with me and made out a $1000 charity contribution to the Tinnitus association in my name. If I want to look him up next time, I'll give him a ring (pun intended).

Monday, July 11: I returned to the employment centre and continued my search for a summer job. Alfonsino was already there, jotting down phone numbers. He nodded in my direction and said, "Hey man, you still lookin' for your nine-to-fiver?"

"Yeah, no luck so far. Hey Afonsino, how did you make out with the stripper job?"

He shrugged, "Bad work environment, man. The women were just too aggressive, look at the scratches!" He pointed to a small scrape on his arm. "I've moved on, I'm gonna take this one, I'm gonna be giving baths to nurses in a Norway bed place," he said as he tapped on a yellow card. After he left, I looked at the card and burst out laughing. He *does* need eyeglasses—it read, "Nurses aide wanted in a geriatric facility in Wolstenholme. Functions: bathing patients, changing bed linen and collecting bedpans." It's not in Norway, but in Quebec, 2000 kilometres north in a small Inuit town!

I found no airplane-related positions except for the ones that were supposed to be "filled." I lowered my standards and picked four places that require no experience, no use of the phone, no spoken French skills and no real communication with the public or co-workers. They were all factory assembly jobs. After Mum answered the phone for the second time today and getting fax machine noises, I told her about my job prospects.

"Ya'll be bored outta yer elbows doing' that kind of work," Mum said as she looked quizzically at the hung-up phone.

"Ya'll do nothin' awl day except to fit pieces together 'n box 'em." She encouraged me to find more interesting jobs but she doesn't know the difficulties I'm going through. She's not deaf and doesn't speak like an Irishman with a blocked nose. I decided not to call via the relay operator and to instead physically go to the potential employers and fill out application forms on site. It was a lot of footwork and my whole afternoon was consumed with taking four busses and walking great distances to out-of-the-way companies. I even got lost at one point. I didn't bother going a forth place because I was exhausted and running out of bus money.

Patrick came home this evening. We showed him around the house and presented him his room in the basement. Dad hung around and interpreted our conversations with our newest family member. I find I'm understanding Patrick more and looking at Dad less. We left him in his room to unpack and

Dad took us aside and explained, "It will be a big adjustment for Patrick and he may show signs of disorientation given he has known and lived the hospital life ever since he was a baby. Living in a real home with fewer restrictions and without being surrounded by chronically ill patients will all be new to him. He will soon go to the Mackay Rehabilitation Centre in their Deaf and hard-of-hearing program to obtain more help. Be patient and give him time."

Tuesday, July 12: I ate breakfast with Patrick and I had to show him where we keep our cereals and bowls. He gobbled up the Pac-man cereal and gave me a thumbs-up. I showed him how to wash the dishes and he taught me the signs for "plate," "cup," "wash," and "boring." He went into his room to read and I cycled to two places I found yesterday on the job postings and filled out their application forms. One secretary at the bigger company told me, after hearing my croaky voice, "Come back when your cold is gone, we don't take sick people."

While I was watching TV a few hours ago, Dad came down and said, "My lad, you have a TTY call." My first TTY call! It was Tilapia! She said she had been trying to reach me for the past couple of days. Apparently, a TTY call is indicated by its sounds of typing, much like a fax machine. I groaned. Damn, that was what Mum heard! I was happy regardless— SHE was trying to call ME! I couldn't believe this, the idea that a girl could have enough interest to call me is beyond me. The only call I've gotten from a girl, besides Demoiselle, was a wrong number. We talked on our TTYs for about a glorious hour and, even better, she invited me to go bowling with her and her friends tomorrow. Tomorrow! Less than 24 hours!

I'll meet her at the shopping centre at 7:00 and we'll meet her friends at 8:30. This means I'll be spending an hour and half with her alone! My stomach doesn't know whether it should performing a quarter half-turn diving move with excitement or a belly flop with nervousness. This was a good time to get that long-overdue help from a big brother. Help he did. I wrote down important words on paper and Patrick showed me how to sign them. Most signs must be accompanied by a proper facial expression, analogous to making voice inflections to spoken words. For example, to sign "Angry," I must show an angry-looking face. When asking a verbal question, your voice goes up at the end of a question, but in ASL, we move our eyebrows either up or down. I learned all the new signs in 30 minutes and Patrick wrote on paper that I have excellent "eye skills". I guess my lifetime of using my eyes in reading lips and rubbery facial expressions are paying off.

Wednesday, July 13: I was excited and active as a bee in a field of flowers all day today. I mowed the lawn, trimmed the hedges and washed the car while thinking of Tilapia and our pending group date. Patrick sat on the deck, reading in the sun and watching me operate the gas mower. I didn't bother applying for wanted jobs to avoid further erosion of my self-esteem. One question ran through my mind while I was mowing down the pesky dandelions: Will she kiss me again? To avoid disappointment, I set low expectations and made myself think that, at the end of the evening, she will punch me in the nose.

I dressed in my best summer clothes and took the bus to Pierrefonds. I arrived 25 minutes early and found Tilapia waiting outside for me. She was dressed in casual clothes and had a yellow T-shirt which read, "I'm not hearing impaired, I'm Deaf!"

"I didn't want to make you wait," she said in her hollow-sounding deaf voice. Tilapia took me to a small ice cream place across the road and while we were sharing a banana split, guess who stepped in? Demoiselle! She was holding hands with that leather-jacketed guy as she got into line and they began to scan the menu on the wall near me. Not wanting her to see me, I turned my head and a piece of nut went down the wrong way. I began to cough and I stood to move my chair away. My foot slipped on a patch of melted ice cream and my other foot went opposite direction. In attempt to regain my balance, my arms and legs flailed in opposite directions and I did moves that would've impressed Karen Kain and Buster Keaton at the same time. I fell forward and made a face-print on the plate-glass window and the nut popped out. I looked back to see Demoiselle standing there with her mouth hanging open as her guy smirked out loud. Jesus! Tilapia strode straight up to the guy and gave him the middle finger into his face; his smirk disappeared. She turned around, helped me up and led me to a table outside.

"Are you all right?" she asked with warm concern in her voice.

"I'll be in five years," I replied.

She rubbed my back and said, "Come on, let's go to the park there."

She carried our banana split as we strolled under the canopy of trees to a park bench and sat facing each other. We finished our dessert and talked. I learned a few more tidbits about her: Her mother is hearing and her father is Deaf and signing. She's the youngest in her family; she has an older hearing sister at home and an older hearing brother who is a certified ASL interpreter living in Edmonton. She graduated from Queen Victoria High School in Westmount after moving back here last year. She got straight As because, "I had an awesome interpreter." She never used an FM system! Next year, she wants study social work in college with the goal of helping Deaf people. While she talked, I gazed at her face in the setting sun, her lips were full and soft, her skin was smooth, her auburn hair was shining. Man—she's beautiful.

Across from us, children were playing on the monkey bars, laughing and yelling. Could she hear their laughter?

"A little, I can see it in their faces."

She pulled back her hair to show she has one hearing aid. "I wear only one so I can ignore half of what my mother says."

She would talk and sign the same time and this helped me to learn a few more new signs. I showed her the signs I learned from Patrick and she was impressed. She even taught me several new ones, such as "friends", "school", "walk", "bowling" and "movie." We met her friends at 8:30 with hugs and backslapping and we all walked over to the bowling lanes.

Watching their hands move in the poetry of sign language made me feel somewhat strange and lost, as if I didn't fully fit in. This was the same old feeling I had whenever I ate dinner with a large group of relatives, where everyone talked at the same time and I would eat in silence, clueless. However, Tilapia would stop sometimes tell me what they were talking about so I never felt ignored and her friends tried to converse with me in simplified ASL. One girl with an earring on her lip, signed, "You're now on Eyeth." I scrunched my face in puzzlement.

She explained, "Hearing people live on EARth, you are now on planet EYEth." So true.

The best moment was when Jim, trying to show off a new move, accidently made the bowling ball bounce over to the next lane. I got the 3rd highest score.

Overall, I found this group of people to be a happy animated bunch with much teasing and joking. Tilapia didn't kiss me in the end, but it didn't matter because I enjoyed myself for the first time in a long time. Tilapia will be driving over to my house tomorrow, not only to visit me but also to meet Patrick. She has a driver's licence!

"Don't look so surprised—deaf people are better drivers and insurance companies know this and sometimes charge less," she said.

I can't wait to see her tomorrow!

Thursday, July 14: Tilapia rang the doorbell at 12:35, the lights flashing in my bedroom while I was working on a new plane model. I gave her a tour of my house and introduced her to Patrick. They enthusiastically conversed in ASL as I stood by, watching the blur of hands and fingers before me. We ate lunch together and they continued to chat. Occasionally, Tilapia would stop and tell me what they've been talking about. I was becoming jealous hearing them laugh and having a good time talking. Sensing my change of mood, Patrick stopped the conversation and said good-bye, which went on for about 15 minutes. Tilapia explained that Deaf people tend to have long good-byes. She said Patrick is smart, witty and good-natured but she noticed he has a severe lack of knowledge about the real world because he was cooped up in the hospital which didn't have close-captioned TVs nor signing staff. My heart skipped beat when she said, "But I like you better," as she squeezed my hand. We talked for about an hour until she had leave for work. She has a part-time job at a restaurant where her only duties are to wash the dishes and clear the tables.

"They don't trust me to take orders," she smiled. At least she has a job. This spurred me to go back to the employment centre. Tomorrow.

Babarosa came by to see Ilisha and when I spied him in the living room, I two-stepped up the stairs before he was able to ask any more inane questions.

As I write this, I can feel loud country and western music being played downstairs. Notice I didn't use the word "heard." My hearing aids are turned off but I felt the pounding beat under my feet and my family jewels are bouncing up and down on the chair like a pair of maracas.

When I went down to make my peanut butter and banana sandwich, I looked at the album Ilisha was listening to and nearly spat out my bite in laughter: it was titled, "*Walk Out Backwards Slowly So I'll Think You're Walking In.*"

Friday, July 15: Tilapia called! We talked for two hours until Mum complained the TTY noise was interrupting her TV movie about the debut of a determined one-legged tightrope walker. Our conversation alternated between her rapid fire typing that zipped along my screen and my plodding one-finger-looking-for-the-next-key typing style. Once she interrupted me with, "Are you eating chips in between letters?" We talked about many different topics and went on frequent tangents. Tilapia asked me out on another date for tomorrow. Wow—just like that. No late-night research at the library, no need for Mum to interpret phone conversations and no awkward chitchats. I'm invited go over to her house for lunch tomorrow at 12.

Saturday, July 16: I took the #211 bus to Tilapia's house in Beaconsfield and found it easily with the precise directions I printed up on my TTY last night. Her directions were mostly visual-based: "When you see the house with blue roof, get off the next stop at the green gas station, my house is the one with the three trees." I rang the doorbell and the last person I expected to see answering the door stood there, in faded jean shorts and tight mid-riff T-shirt.

"Hi Eggie, so you're dating my sister?" Molly smiled. I stared at her blankly. "Come off it, I knew you were deaf all along, you never fooled me. Nobody stares at my lips like you do, most guys' eyes are roaming all over my body!'"

This explains why she was so easy to understand and lip-read! Tilapia came down the stairs and stood next to Molly, "Hi Egg, I see you met my sister," she signed and voiced at the same time.

"Go away," she motioned to Molly who huffed and went up the stairs. "That was Molly," she fingerspelled M-o-l-l-y. "She's trouble." I knew exactly what she meant.

She showed me around her house. She lives in a large spacious home, bigger than mine but with a smaller yard. Her parents were pleased to meet me, beaming great smiles and doling out hearty handshakes. Tilapia and I ate a lunch on her deck under a warm sun and cool breeze. She explained her upbringing and Deaf culture. "The Deaf community is made up a many deaf people connected for one reason: they all "speak" the same language—sign language. For us, our hearing impairment isn't a 'disability,' but a major part of our identity. Many of us grow up in residential Deaf-only schools far from home, rarely wear hearing aids and actually proud of our deafness. We have our own culture, just as any other culture and have our own values, beliefs and customs. We have our own political organizations, curling teams, dance troupes and so on. There's even a Deaf pilot's club!"

I smiled at this and asked, "Do they live on the same streets or near each other?"

"No, Deaf people don't live in the same areas as seen in the Italian communities in big cities and may even live far from each other but they find ways to keep in touch, even before TTYs. Socializing with each other is an important part of Deaf culture, and you know, it's hard for us to socialize with hearing people so we are more inclined to hang out with others like us." I knew I was missing something from my life.

She took a bite of her sandwich and continued, "You know, since it's a culture in itself, 'Deaf' is spelt with a big 'D' because it's a proper noun. Many Deaf people grew up together in the same Deaf schools and know each other well, so gossip and rumours can fly over the proverbial fence from one set of hands to another as quickly as do among hearing folks in small towns. I've been backstabbed a few times," she looked down. "But it's still worth being part of it."

I thought for a moment and spoke up, "What about deaf people who speak?"

She paused, "Oral deaf people can speak but choose not to sign. They see themselves having an impairment and disability, have no "Deaf culture" although they do loosely associate with each other. They wear hearing aids, go to hearing schools and try to fit in with the hearing world." Sounds like yours truly. For many years, I saw my deafness as a problem and never even had a slightest inkling that it could be part of who I am.

Tilapia looked at me and put her hand gently on my forearm, "You know, Egg, when you take your hearing aids off night, you're Deaf." A bird flew up from the ground towards the sunny blue sky.

"Oh—wait here, I gotta go in to get more milk." She left me alone for a good few minutes. As I breathed in the air filled with a fresh laundry smell, I closed my eyes and turned my face towards the bright warm sun and savoured the blissful serenity. In my mind, I saw a tranquil images of a brook flowing steadily around the smooth stones and a school of shimmering fish swimming together downstream. For the first time in a long time, I felt at peace with myself despite the recent chaos. Everything will be all right in my world.

I cannot express how much this conversation, along with my experiences with her and her friends, have influenced me and how I thought of myself. When I bade her goodbye, I rode the bus home, went in my bedroom, lied down on my bed and thought about what Tilapia said. I can talk but yet, I want to learn more ASL and be with both Deaf people and hearing people—I'm at a fork in the road. You know what? I gotta compromise. The middle road is best; I've the best of both worlds. I can be with both hearing and Deaf people. A new excitement grew inside me along with a sense of satisfaction of a new road taken. I'm a deaf person, period, not a lumberjack wanna-be or a person with defective hearing stumbling around in the darkness trying to find the light switch in a hearing world. What's more, I'm not "hearing impaired." It sounds too much like "impaired driving" and "deaf" has a nice, short ring to it.

This is it. I've decided to stop writing any more journal entries. Much is going to happen to me from this day on since I've found my "home." I've spent too many nights staying up past midnight writing these daily events and it's time I put down my pen. First, I think I will go make myself a peanut butter and banana sandwich.

Marc Heyez

71336520R00164

Made in the USA
Columbia, SC
28 May 2017